The Potter's Wheel

How Epilepsy Changed My Life

By: George L. Choyce

This is a journal for those who are grieving the loss
of something significant or someone special.

THE POTTER'S WHEEL:
How Epilepsy Changed My Life

For information, contact BDI Publishers, Atlanta, Georgia, bdipublishers@gmail.com.

BDI Publishers

ISBN: 978-0-9970445-4-6
FIRST EDITION

Layout by Tudor Maier
Front Cover Design by Andrew Fuller Choyce

BDI Publishers
Atlanta, Georgia

Encouragement to Tell My Story

My story is not really a story about epilepsy as it is about one person's spiritual struggle of how to move forward in a positive and healthy manner when life throws something at you that is completely unexpected. My story, however, is unusual. How does an Episcopal Priest move forward when they cannot get their seizures under control? I found the following quotes to be an accurate summary to the diverse means of encouragement to tell this story. They range from professional to personal.

"George, you have been through something extremely traumatic. No one is going to deny that. How you proceed from here will make all the difference. It is now up to you as to how you move forward ..." The final words I remember of my therapist after three months of sessions.

"I hope that one day you will reach the point that you channel your anger and do something positive with it. George, it will change you and maybe change someone else for the better ..." The final words I remember of a neuropsychologist who tested me for cognitive functioning.

"George, you have a story to tell. You need to tell it. People need to read it." — Clergy Colleagues

"You need to keep fighting because people like us need you in this world." — Mary Jane Post

"George, you're a good writer. So share your story and give people some hope." — Anne Choyce

Dedication:

I dedicate this book to my Lord and Savior, Jesus Christ. Additionally, this book is dedicated to Neil, Drew, Kelly, and Preston Choyce who have given up so much to live with their dad who has epilepsy. By default they live with my epilepsy and live with it gracefully with humor and honesty. Finally, I see Jesus most clearly through Anne, the woman I go through this life with, as she continually chooses to go through this life with me. On this night, December 23, 2014, I found a letter she wrote to me last Christmas. The letter reminded me of all of our dreams, from serious to funny and to everything in-between. There is still so much to go as long as we go together "in sickness and in health" all beginning with "In the Name of God."

Forward

The Reverend George Choyce is an Episcopal priest with epilepsy. He is a priest by call and by ordination. While epilepsy derailed his career, it has not taken his priesthood. He is a priest and this book is part of the work of a priest with epilepsy doing ministry. In these pages, he shares not only an honest account of his struggle to come to terms with this disease and how he has been transformed by the struggle, but he offers understanding and hope for all who have been struck by the darkness that enters our lives like a thief in the night. As Easter people, as people of the resurrection, we are people who look for new life. George is learning to live again, different than before, but living the resurrection he has been given as an incarnation of God's hope for all who have found their dreams dashed and their lives shaken and turned upside down.

—The Rev. William L. Breedlove, Ph.D.

Chapter One

Dreams and Real Life

*I form light and create darkness, I make weal and create woe;
I the Lord do these things.* Isaiah 45:7 NRSV

*O God our heavenly Father, you have blessed us and given us
dominion over all the earth: Increase our reverence before the
mystery of life; and give us new insight into your purposes
for the human race, and new wisdom and determination
in making provision for its future in accordance with your
will; through Jesus Christ our Lord.* Amen. The Book of
Common Prayer, p. 828

The date of November 22, 1963, is recognizable to
most of us. On this date, there were two different
dreams. The first was the birth of the All-American
dream; the second was the death of the All-American
dream.

You know the second dream — a nightmare to be more
accurate — don't you? In the dream, there was a parade,
a convertible limousine, a waving of royal hands if there
were such a thing as American-born royalty in the United
States. In the nightmare, there was a gunshot, a slumped
body, a half-crazed woman crawling out of the backseat

and onto the trunk of the limousine within a chaotic, discordant, surreal symphony of frantic fingers flapping toward a window of the Dallas Book Depository.

Camelot was over in less than a second. A bullet had pierced the skin, skull, and brain of John Fitzgerald Kennedy, and just like that, the 35th President of the United States was dead. His life was over. There is no poetry here to take away the brutality and finality of the death of a dream. It seemed all of the citizens of the United States were pinning their hopes and dreams on this larger-than-life President, nicknamed "Jack," also known as JFK. He lost his life in Dallas, Texas.

In Atlanta, Georgia, on the other hand, a young couple both smiled and sweated as they signed official looking papers. With the simple stroke of a black ballpoint pen, the dream of homeownership was theirs. There was an additional element of a dream that day for the woman held a baby tightly yet tenderly in her freckled arms from years of living in Florida. Somewhere deep down, perhaps in what one could call her soul, she too was pinning her hopes and dreams on someone who just happened to be a smaller-than-life baby. This life was two months and five days old.

I am this child. This couple had a healthy baby and a new house. Everything was perfectly in place for their Camelot of "and they lived happily ever after." Life has a way of getting in the way of well-planned dreams like that. I had plans too. A death of sorts happened along the way, but a story is born.

"George, you have a story to tell. Now tell it." Some utterance of that literal quote has been stated in a prayer-like tone that comes close to reverence by numerous folks from a diversity of backgrounds. For instance, some of my clergy colleagues have kindly confirmed the "story to tell" statement. With very little exception, the number and variety of people to whom I have told the story have resoundingly echoed my colleagues' sentiments: "George, you have to tell people about this." Furthermore, one of my chief delights is when others hear of the effect of my neurological condition upon my priestly vocation, they exclaim in all manner of pronunciations and varying degrees of volume, "Wow, George. You've got to let people know about this. You've got a story to tell."

Reflecting on those words, I am humbled and embarrassed. Humbled because I have been encouraged to write and tell my story by such an eclectic conglomeration of humanity. Embarrassed by my naïveté to pastoral opportunity because I would have encouraged anyone else to write this story if it was their story. But it is my story that was conceived in the structure of a handwritten diary of sorts and then born into a journal for all to read.

The story starts with a healthy baby boy being born in 1963 in Atlanta, Georgia. My story was simply the way suburbia was "supposed" to be. Mom was the homemaker; Dad was an attorney. We had a maid. I went to private school. I played football and excelled at it. Everything was going according to the predictable plan until the unexpected occurred.

Chapter Two

A Boy's Discovery on a Football Field

O Lord, you have searched me and known me. Psalm 139:1

God our Father, you see your children growing up in an unsteady and confusing world: Show them that your ways give more life than the ways of the world, and that following you is better than chasing after selfish goals. Help them to take failure, not as a measure of their worth, but as a chance for a new start. Give them strength to hold their faith in you, and to keep alive their joy in your creation; through Jesus Christ our Lord. Amen. BCP, p. 829

On his football helmet was a two-inch wide, six-inch long piece of white trainer's tape with big, black, bold letters that read "A Parker." This is what I remembered his name to be. This was August. This was a time that no breeze could be tempted to blow across the uneven, dry and dusty excuse of a practice football field where football hopefuls vied for a spot on a team. About one hundred of us were gathered for football tryouts. Since there was no wind, our perspiration doubled. It dribbled from soaked pockets of padding inside our helmets thereby producing a squeaky sound and a sweaty smell every time a head was rotated left to right and back again, as well as up and down.

I was eight. It was third grade for those of us who were trying out for the Little Division in the Pop Warner football league that also featured the division of Pee Wee and Big. On that August day, those of us trying out for the football teams in the Little category wore those official pieces of tape tautly stretched across the front of our pathetic plastic helmets. "G Choice" was on mine. I was used to this by now. The teachers, coaches, even Sunday School Superintendents usually misspelled my last name to read "Choice."

The intonation of "Choyce" and "Choice" was identical. Coaches would boom out our Sire name, "Choice" or "Jones" or "Smith" — they were barked out since we were now "men." For example, "Choice, drop and give me ten," referred to pushups. "Choice, run a 'down and out,'" referred to a pass pattern. It was all part of a harmless semi-hazing, coming-of-age ritual that was all a part of being "drafted" to a football team. I was a talented player and was drafted in the first round.

What I remember was that I did not much care for Alan Parker. My negative feelings towards Alan were due to the fact he beat me in every football drill of the tryouts; he was even drafted ahead of me. What's more, he was stronger at pushups. He ran a faster "down and out." Objectively, he outperformed me in every drill of skill. I did not like him for the shallow reason that he was better than I was at playing football.

Plain and simple, I was jealous. Being both beaten and jealous was something that I was not used to at all. Plain and simple, I did not want to get used to the off-putting phenomena of losing. An eight-year-old by the name of George Choyce, not G Choice, was coming face-to-face with the grim reality that you cannot always win.

Life up unto that point was really quite simple and straightforward: practice hard and play hard. The result was that you would win. And I did all of those things, and I did win football games. It was as uncomplicated as one plus one equals two. It was black and white. It was simplistic and typical of an eight-year-old mind. There was no space for ambiguity or mystery in my young mind.

I remember that Alan was drafted by the Little Bears, and I was drafted to the Little Colts. The fact was that that year the Bears handily beat the Colts. The fact was that the scoreboard read Home 21 and Visitor 7. There it was in literal yet fading black metal and flickering white lights for all to see. The reality was that the Bears beat the Colts by the score of 21 to 7. All of these facts once again added up to negative feelings. Who cared about being a good sport? Plain and simple, we lost. The point — the sole point — of the game was to win. Plain and simple, winning was all that mattered. You do not get a trophy for being a good and fair sport. Being a good and fair sport was for the puny Pee Wees.

It was at the last game of the year that something else began to matter other than the score. The last game of the season arrived in mid-December. It brought with it temperatures that were out-of-the-ordinary for those of us who were raised in Georgia. It was in the low thirties on that December morning. Something happened at that last game which made the temperature uncomfortably plunge even more than any thermometer could measure.

Prior to the playing of a poppy and scratchy version of the National Anthem, the announcer asked for all of our attention. I do not remember his exact words, but I do remember the message. He announced that Alan Parker had been killed in a car wreck when his grandfather had had a heart attack and driven off a bridge on the way to the Florida Keys. Alan had drowned. Alan was dead.

It was as if something had tackled the cold wintry padding of my football helmet. Ice, instead of sweat, rattled down. Nausea took me over. I lost my innocence about life and death at the age of nine now, right then and there on the fifty-yard line in a neighborhood park called Chastain Park.

It was as if something that was supposed to be as simple and straightforward as study hard and play hard no longer applied. Of course, old people were supposed to die. I was not so naïve as to think that no one dies. The crisis was that people my age were not supposed to die. That was not a part of the plan.

The plan. The plan. The plan. The plan is the world of "ought to", and "supposed to be" where well-rehearsed idioms are employed to keep the world under the fantasy of control. It is not a bad thing this idea of a plan. It is just unrealistic.

My parents were doing what other suburban parents do. They wanted me safe from the cruelty of the outside world.

The outside world, nevertheless, scales its way over the white picket fences, marches upon the manicured lawns and invades even burglar-alarmed houses of suburbia. It even makes its way onto the football fields filled with happy children playing in neighborhood parks.

At the announcement of Alan's death, the bubble of the "burbs" was popped. My old normal died that day and was soundly routed by reality. A new normal was born in the brittle brown grass of Chastain Park. The new normal was a world where one plus one began to equal zero. Actually, his death did not add up. Psychologically, his death did not make sense. Emotionally, his death was not rational.

I had no coping mechanism to deal with my new normal. I found myself in complete denial that Alan had died. "Let us now have a moment of silence for Alan Parker," was all that I can recall of the announcement made through that crackly speaker. The game then began.

Chapter Three

A Young Man's Discovery on the Field of Life

... and the two shall become one flesh. So they are no longer two, but one flesh. Therefore what God has joined together, let no one separate. — Mark 10:8-9 NRSV

" ... to have and to hold from this day forward, for better for worse, for richer for poorer, in sickness and in health, to love and to cherish, until we are parted by death. This is my solemn vow." BCP, p. 427

Just days after their final exams from college, two recently-graduated seniors simply stared at one another in front of the altar of the Cathedral of St. Philip in Atlanta, Georgia, and repeated those words to one another. The entire "solemn vow" began with the phrase "In the Name of God." There were 150 people in the pews witnessing their vow. Two clergy — one Episcopal and the other Presbyterian — were even in closer proximity to that young couple. The couple and the clergy were twelve and ten feet away respectively from a massive marble altar.

At this point, all of the fidgeting ceased. Silence penetrated sacred space. Occasionally, some of the eyewitnesses noiselessly raised tissues to dab at their moist eyes. There was absolute quiet except for the words that the young couple vowed to one another. Those words would become literal in the years to come. "In sickness and in health" was not a figure of speech.

What brought them to this point? Though they were in front of the altar in a magnificent Cathedral, it was not Camelot. They were not Faux- American royalty, nor did they even pretend to be. They were simply Anne Statham and George Choyce, who wanted to spend the rest of their lives together.

Alan's death brought Anne and me together, though I have never put that together until now. How did I come to that connection? For one thing, the tragedy of Alan's early demise, as strange and heartless as this may sound, became a gift. His gift to me, and to others on the Little Colts, is that we learned early on that life is not fair. It is worth repeating —life is not fair. It is not a cliché.

Innocence died in the instant of a crackled announcement over a loudspeaker. Something was wounded within me on the football field that had nothing to do with the sting associated with a cheap-shot tackle in chilly December. Simply to know someone was at risk of being emotionally injured. I became more calculating in relationships. Eventually, I left childhood behind and was thrust into adolescence. I grew up. Anne grew up with her own experiences.

Anne and I had been through our separate disasters of dating, drinking, and drugs. When we met, though there was romance, infatuation, and outright being "head over heels in love," we were also realistic. We had been wounded by life. The chemical blast of hormones was there, of course, but the blast of hormones stood in tandem with the smack of reality. That smack from our own separate realities formed us as individuals and then formed us as a couple. The two became one.

In our relationship, there was no Prince Charming. There was no Damsel in Distress held in the topmost tower guarded by a dragon. There was no Camelot. There was no "happily ever after." Right then and right there in front of that altar, a holy bond was forged in the cauldron of the reality of all of our past experiences. Alan Parker's death gave us life in the mysterious process that leads to becoming husband and wife. Reality gave us commitment, which we were going to need, especially when it came again and again to the "in sickness and in health" part of our vows. I am convinced that the lead-in phrase of "In the Name of God" deserves the credit.

Throughout this journal, you will see God, the Church, and priesthood mentioned quite a bit. I am still trying to work through all three of these relationships separately and together. My brain changed. And so did everything else. The Potter's Wheel melding my brain continues to spin because the journey is not over.

In addition to this, Anne is an intricate part of the diversity associated with all of the Institutional Church and God relationships. That is due to the fact that after we had been married, I pursued ordination. Here is what happened:

Chapter Four

Delightful and Dubious Detours

I will lead the blind by a road they do not know, by paths they have not known I will guide them ... and I will not forsake them. Isaiah 42:16

O God, by whom the meek are guided in judgment, and light riseth up in darkness for the godly: Grant us, in all our doubts and uncertainties, the grace to ask what thou wouldest have us to do, that the Spirit of wisdom may save us from all false choices, and that in thy light we may see light, and in thy straight path may not stumble; through Jesus Christ our Lord. Amen. BCP, p. 832

"**G**eorge, take some time to experience life and then come back and see me," the Bishop said with a spontaneous yawn and a casual stretch of his arms going upward while leaning back in his office chair. He then leaned forward as his leather chair clunked, folded his arms on the desk and looked me dead in the eye and repeated, "Come back and see me then."

Staring at him through stunned eyes, as my heart's tempo escalated and with an instantly cotton-mouthed tongue, I uttered two quick questions. "When would you recommend I come back and see you," I asked but then quickly supplied my answer, "like in a few years?"

He chuckled and replied, "When you're thirty." And he meant it. There was, however, no chuckle for me at the age of 22. He would be retired by that time.

This was my abrupt welcome to the fickle ordination process in the Episcopal Church. Ordination was not like practicing harder than other members of the team. Ordination was neither a test one could pass by studying harder, although there is an intense three-year academic portion of the process called seminary. Ordination was a personal process, a community process, a discernment process that meant other people would be involved in the whether or not you were called to be a priest. The ordination process was like nothing I had ever experienced.

I did not want to experience more life with the "come back and see me" elusiveness nagging at me. Uncertainty was also a phenomenon I was not used to. A better word for uncertainty would be ambiguity, which took Anne and me from the Diocese (geographical area) of Atlanta unambiguously to the Diocese of Central Florida. We moved in 1987 to Vero Beach, Florida. Trinity Episcopal Church employed me as their Youth Minister.

I entered the ordination process again. The Diocese of Central Florida had a variation of philosophy when it came to experiencing life. The age of twenty-four was plenty old enough to pursue seminary according to their discernment process.

In 1989, Anne and I moved yet again. This time we went north to Alexandria, Virginia, to attend the Protestant Episcopal Theological Seminary in Virginia, as it is officially known. Unofficially, the Protestant Episcopal Theological Seminary in Virginia is known as PETS, VTS, Virginia Theological Seminary, Virginia Seminary or simply "Virginia." A Dean from another seminary, whom Anne and I had met when we were searching for Graduate School, accurately described the seminary experience. He stated, "Seminary is like standing under a waterfall with a paper cup trying to catch all of the water."

Seminary was indeed like that. The waterfall was real. The cascade of water was the academics and the relationships with faculty, other students, as well as their families. The gush of water was the incredible, complex, and beautiful worship on campus, as well as in Virginia, the District of Columbia, and Maryland. The dance of water was the Fighting Flamingos' flag football team. The torrent of water was the seemingly vast array of recreational and historical day trips and overnights that the area offered. On the other hand, the cup was my ability to take it all in.

For one of the first times in my life, it really was okay to have that metaphorical cup as my ability, or lack thereof. To one degree or another, my classmates were in the same circumstances. We were bound by that metaphorical cup of seminary experience and held it out at the same time. The difference was in the contents of our individual cups that were caught in the descending current. Some cups were filled primarily with academics while others were brimming with pastoral care. Some cups were bubbling up with the foam of "smooze," which I define as the short-lived and shallow employment of charm and good looks to get almost anything one wants. Some cups were filled with an enigmatic complexity of ingredients that formed leadership — impossible to define, but real. In other words, you knew leadership when you were in the presence of a leader.

My cup was a mix. Through the experience of the filling of my cup in seminary — and it was an experience — I learned that it was okay to be a "B" student for a Masters of Divinity degree. Along the way, I was doing what my first Bishop counseled me to do. I was experiencing life. I was learning in the most expansive sense of the word. The academic grade "B" was fine when you were getting an "A" in experience. Along the way, our first child, Neil came into our lives in 1991 — an "A" in experience!

The synopsis is that the discernment process leads to the experience of seminary which leads to ordination. Ordination is the end of an extensive and exhausting process and the commencement of another. It is here that I have to be honest and literally confess that ordination was, at its worst, a career stepping stone to what I considered the prestigious positions of ordained ministry. This was confirmed recently by a colleague of mine who said another priest described me as "impeccably dressed, always having his act together, yet somewhat aloof." In other words, I actually did look the part but was to some scope distant in relationships.

I think that this journal helps me to "exorcise my demons" of an unhealthy ego. Planting it in the fertile soil of writing for all to see is good for my soul. Placing healthy ego instances in this text are also good for my soul. For instance, there were far more times when and where priesthood was exercised with compassion, sermons were delivered with inspiration, and the sacraments celebrated with dignified conviction than there were times of selfish ambition. I was a good and faithful priest regardless of my aspirations.

Chapter Five

The Ladder Rungs Start to Splinter

Pride goes before destruction, and a haughty spirit before a fall. Proverbs 16:18

The Lord Jesus, after he had supped with his disciples and had washed their feet, said to them, "Do you know what I, your Lord and Master, have done to you? I have given you an example, that you should do as I have done." BCP, p. 274 Maundy Thursday Liturgy

---

I was, however, on an undeniable track to become a Bishop, a Dean of a Cathedral, or a Cardinal Rector. The protocol of climbing the ecclesiastical ladder of success was being observed in the minutest detail. I am simply being candid here. Those of you who are feeling smug right now, well go right ahead and "cast the first stone."

I had placed my foot on the first rung of the ecclesiastical ladder by accepting my first call out of seminary to be the Assistant to the Rector of St. Andrew's Episcopal Church on St. Andrew Bay in Panama City, Florida close to the time of Hurricane Andrew. Seven months after Hurricane Andrew, another Andrew entered into the picture. Our second child, Andrew, was born here in March of 1993. Drew, as he began to be called, was surrounded by Andrews all of the time.

I scaled to the second rung of the ladder when Anne and I moved our expanding family to Pittsburgh, Pennsylvania. This move above the Mason-Dixon Line was in response to a call for ministry where I served as an Assistant Priest at Calvary Episcopal Church. Our only daughter, Kelly, was born in 1995 in Pittsburgh during March and in a snowstorm.

The third step was a significant one. We moved from Pennsylvania to Newington, Connecticut, where I served as the Rector of Grace Episcopal Church. Being Rector of a Church is literally a "significant step" in one's call to priesthood because it entails a remarkable amount of responsibility that Assistants do not have. Our fourth child, Preston, was born in New Britain, Connecticut, in December of 1998. He was born — you guessed it, in a New England snowstorm.

The Choyces had run the gamut of Hurricanes to snowstorms, of the "Redneck Riviera" in Panama City to Yankees in Connecticut, to "y'all" in Florida, "y'unz" in Pittsburgh, and "hey you" in Connecticut. I then took the biggest step of all to the fourth rung that placed me almost at the top of the clergy career ladder. I was called to be the Rector of St. Timothy's Episcopal Church on Signal Mountain, Tennessee.

It was during this period from 1992 to 2011 that I began to believe my own press. Parishioners at St. Andrew's, Calvary, Grace and St. Timothy's would speak similar sentiments yet in the dissimilar accents of Southern, Midwestern and Yankee:

"It's just a matter of time before you're elected Bishop if you keep preaching like that."

"You'll be Dean of the Cathedral when they discover our fine worship."

"We know that we're going to lose you to another Episcopal Church if our numbers continue to grow."

A Bishop friend of mine went so far as to say, "George, it is not if you will be Bishop. The only question is when?"

St. Andrew's, Calvary, Grace and St. Timothy's first appear to be a disjointed mix. There is, nevertheless a pattern which goes like this: 1) Assistant at a medium sized parish; 2) Assistant at a large parish; 3) Rector of a medium-sized parish, and 4) Rector of a growing medium to large parish. Assistant, Assistant, Rector, and Rector were all substantial rungs on an ecclesiastical ladder to reaching the top and becoming a Bishop, a Dean of a Cathedral, or a Cardinal Rector.

Here is but one revealing episode: If there is such a thing as knowing where I've been, it is being "recruited" by two prestigious churches in 2011 to enter their search processes to being completely discouraged and almost rejected to enter a deeply distressed church's search process in 2012.

That's where I've been in my Vocation as a priest. For instance, a large and prominent Cathedral invited me, via beautiful stationery, into their search process. Moreover, my name was proposed by a Bishop, on thick-stocked paper, from a prominent pool of other priests across the country to enter the search process of a high-status church. Once my brain began to betray me, I was sent via email that a Search Committee from a totally troubled church had already discerned that I did not have a call to be their priest, though I could re-enter their search process. In other words, this whole process of grieving has been quite humbling, although involuntarily so.

Where am I going? What am I now? Who am I since priesthood? has always been so much of my identity. Though I am an Episcopal Priest with my uncontrolled condition, this story is written from my specific and personal point of view. All I know is that I am a description of the title, as are the millions who suffer from a multitude of neurological issues. Our lives spin. The lives of those who care for us spin. Control is lost. There is loss. Since grief is universal, however, all of us are a part of the grief process when we experience a loss. Grief is how we cope with loss.

My well-planned, ought to be, supposed to be, life had been working. I had practiced hard, studied harder, and worked hardest along the way to my understanding of prestigious positions. It was all coming together. I was climbing the ladder of ecclesiastical success. I was almost at the top. And I was about to fall far from the upper rungs of the make-believe ladder. We will now fast forward to scenarios that read drastically different from the organized chronology of my past.

When through fiery trials thy pathway shall lie,

My grace, all sufficient, shall be thy supply;

The flame shall not hurt thee; I only design

Thy dross to consume, and thy gold to refine.

"How Firm a Foundation" by John Rippon

Chapter Six

Oh, Good Grief

My brothers and sisters, whenever you face trials of any kind, consider it nothing but joy, because you know that the testing of your faith produces endurance; and let endurance have its full effect, so that you may be mature and complete, lacking in nothing. James 1:2-4

Almighty and everliving God, in your tender love for the human race you sent your Son our Savior Jesus Christ to take upon him our nature, and to suffer death upon the cross, giving us the example of his great humility: Mercifully grant that we may walk in the way of his suffering, and also share in his resurrection; through Jesus Christ our Lord, who lives and reigns with you and the Holy Spirit, one God for ever and ever. Amen. BCP, p. 272

THE STAGES OF GRIEF

American Psychiatrist, Dr. Elisabeth Kubler-Ross, wrote a seminal book in 1969 entitled *On Death and Dying*. In this groundbreaking work, she identified five widely-accepted distinct stages of grief: Denial, Anger, Bargaining, Depression, and Acceptance. I find that though these stages are clinically accurate in progression, it does not rule out the paradoxical fact that feelings can take you backwards in the grieving process.

People are complex and contradictory. And grieving is not a perfectly linear process. Put those two observations together. You will now read about some of the complexity and inconsistency of humanity through the lens of a real and raw person who is living with a common brain condition. But fair warning, what you read from here on out is authentic and not watered down to make it more palatable and acceptable in a "happily ever after" ending.

STAGE I - DENIAL

"It didn't happen."

"Not that I know of."

"It just felt weird."

"I felt I was experiencing another person's thoughts and emotions."

"It was like waking up but not from sleep."

"I didn't even know I had had one and simply picked up where I left off."

The previous quotes were what I engaged time and time again as a way to cope with my neurological circumstances.

Chapter Seven

The First Hint Something was Wrong

I praise you, for I am fearfully and wonderfully made. Psalm 139:14

Assist us mercifully, O Lord, in these our supplications and prayers, and dispose the way of thy servants towards the attainment of everlasting salvation; that, among the changes and chances of this mortal life, they may ever be defended by thy gracious and ready help; through Jesus Christ our Lord. Amen. BCP, p. 832

O n a Summer Sunday, there was no supernatural sign or even an objective forewarning that something out-of-the-ordinary would transpire in my life. On this day, the fog rolled in for the first time in my brain. There were 120 onlookers who were eyewitnesses to the event. They were baffled to abruptly find themselves in an uncomfortable fog of silence while I was elevated in a pulpit and standing in front of them. You cannot veil it from that quantity of people. It was the first day my brain betrayed me.

The setting was in a church. The context was that of a sermon and Episcopalians expect a twelve to fifteen-minute sermon, give or take a minute or two. This particular sermon was almost over, which meant it was about at the twelve-minute-mark. It was awkward what happened next. I simply stopped speaking or preaching.

Here is what I wrote from my personal perception:

It was both a weird and wonderful sensation as I remained standing but lost consciousness while entering into a trancelike state. The experience was both dreamlike peaceful, yet distinctly out-of-context and unsettling for being almost at the conclusion of a sermon and experiencing whatever it was that was happening to me. For a full minute and a half, I simply stood there in the pulpit, tapped the microphone several times asking, "Is this thing on?" and then had a sluggish return or a reawakening sensation to exactly where I had left off in the sermon. There was no doubt in my mind that I had lost my place in the sermon, but there was, what I thought at the time, a graceful recovery from a five to seven-second stumble. I resumed the sermon as if nothing had happened.

After the "amen" that ended the sermon, I returned to my seat a full ten feet behind the altar. I sat down, stood up just seconds later and then said in a perfectly normal voice, "Let us stand and affirm our faith in the words of the Nicene Creed." This is the standard sequence of events in the worship. To top off the absurdity of the situation, I had absolutely no idea that my brain had manifested that something was off beam.

The liturgy went forward as planned, yet I could not fail to detect that something was not quite right, or was that just some paranoia on my part? I also felt upset for no apparent reason. As the Assistant Priest set the altar for communion, I whispered to the Associate Rector rather jokingly, "You know I felt a little fuzzy up there in the pulpit." The gaze of hard-to-hide shock in her eyes told the story that it was something far from me "feeling a little fuzzy up in the pulpit." Something was wrong; very, very wrong indeed for the time being.

As outlandish as it might seem, I really did not know that I had even had one, only that there was an abnormal disappearance of an unbelievably brief amount of time. I perceived the entire event as five to seven seconds of spacing out and losing my place in the sermon. It was not until the Associate Rector, who witnessed the event, had something to say about it that I realized something disturbingly out-of-the-ordinary had occurred. I think the distressing query, "George, what in the world happened up there," was about the gist of it. With an anxious look, she continued, "You were up there for a minute and a half. Occasionally you tapped the microphone and asked, 'Is this thing on?' George, it made no sense. You just stood there and spoke disconnected phrases. I was about to come up there and get you down from the pulpit."

Denial goes deep. I believed her but could not believe that some bizarre episode had happened. I don't have a brain condition. Other people have it. The incident, nevertheless, was neurological in nature, heart-like in emotion, nonetheless, spiritually it was like having your soul torn in two. It was visceral. It hurt, but the pain was not contained to a certain part of my body; the pain permeated throughout. Furthermore, it is not just the person who has had one for the first time who denies it; oftentimes, the person or people who are witnesses to it dismiss it too. It is an absurd denial strategy born from contagion.

On the other hand, what occurred that Sunday a.m. was such a paradigmatic overreaction to the *nth* degree for just a couple of seconds of confusion is what I thought as the worship service went forward. What was going on here? Why were there disturbed and uncomfortable stares that were speaking in their silence of stigma? Why were there petite, as well as isolated of pockets of undertones breaking out? Why was there an inexplicable and uncomfortable aura of "unholiness" permeating the Holy space? This whole absurd incident had to be an incarnate textbook case of cognitive dissonance.

For example, I proceeded to greet parishioners like everything was normal at the end of the church service simply by speaking my typical "go to" and well-rehearsed lines of "Good morning" and "Have a nice day." They were the tried and true token exchanges of the twenty or so years of experience in being a priest. I even hate to put it down in writing for you to read of the lightheartedness of some of my post-worship dialogue, but you were cautioned earlier on that I was going to be honest.

Deny, deny, and then keep on denying was the strategy, and almost all were in on the cover-up. The small amount of handshakes, I noticed, was hastened. Hardly any out of 120 parishioners inquired, "George, are you okay?" The few who greeted me were, nevertheless, much quicker than usual to move through the line and rush onward to the buffet at the Golf Club or to their next activity. I should mention that these are the classic good and caring people who hastened through the line. We were all trying to cope with the incident in the pulpit through the strategy of the "elephant-in-the-living-room" syndrome. Simply ignore the elephant, and it will go away.

Those who did stay gathered in small circles. My stomach clenched watching this phenomenon take place, and by this time, queasiness took over denial. They were talking about me. Something had happened. Now I knew it. Again, I was experiencing something like cognitive dissonance. One person became two. Although I had this belief that I was normal and healthy, something completely abnormal and unhealthy had occurred some moments earlier. My worldview had been shattered in the space of less than two hours by a neurological event that took place in the context of worship in front of compassionate people. My worldview had been shattered once more. Some forty years later, it was Alan Parker's death all over again. Something happened that was not supposed to happen.

Back in my office after the eleven o'clock service, the Associate Rector began to fill me in on the specifics of what had actually ensued in the pulpit. Though one part of me believed her, another piece would not and could not accept what she was relaying to me. Denial, denial, and more denial. What an intense internal battle that was. There was no reason for her to make this kind of thing up. This must be a bad joke, but how could so many people be in on it? Whatever had happened to me in the pulpit was, in my opinion, like some sort of collective hallucination and people were just exaggerating what had happened. Well, that was my feeble justification of the whole situation.

Denial, denial, and more and more denial was my nonsensical strategy of surviving an insane situation. So what did I do? I simply left the church, got in my car and went on with my ordinary day to do some errand to take my mind off of whatever it was that had just happened. I cringe when reflecting on what it would have been like to have had that first one behind the wheel of my car.

This errand to cope and take my mind off of what had occurred earlier was to pick up a prescription for my spouse, Anne. She had had rotator cuff surgery four days earlier. I drove over to the pharmacy to pick up a refill on her pain medication. I was obsessively and silently repeating, "I'm OK. I'm just tired. I'm OK, just tired."

To interrupt my obsessive thoughts of "OK, just tired" while waiting for the prescription to get filled, I skulked over to the blood pressure machine, peeled off my jacket, rolled up the right sleeve of my black clergy shirt, pressed my arm through the blood pressure cup, squashed down the "Start" button and took my blood pressure. Slowly, the band tightened. It made a crunching noise. The screen on the techno-machine then read 150 systolic over 100 diastolic. This reading was some forty-five minutes to an hour after my brain fog event. I wondered what my blood pressure was at the time. My pulse measured 80 according to the machine. What was it earlier? Literally, God only knows.

After taking my blood pressure and pulse, I thought, "Well, at least this explains it." It was some verifiable evidence, some concrete proof of what was going on in my body. The stress — the good and bad stress of everything had finally taken its toll and was manifesting itself in high blood pressure. Ha. It's just high blood pressure. It's just stinking high blood pressure. What a relief. Whew! It was time to go home and have a beer.

I do not wish to come across as the least bit patronizing, but being a clergyperson is a high-stress vocation that is complicated by the fact that most do not perceive it as a high-stress vocation. What could be more peaceful than getting paid for praying and preaching? What could be easier than getting your prayers from a book and searching the internet for sermon material? What could be nicer than to be nice to nice people, although not everyone is nice — including this priest — all of the time?

The blood pressure machine initiated a plan to take control of my health. I would schedule an appointment with my Primary Care Physician, run some tests, and get on a low dose of a prescription to combat my high blood pressure. I would be in control again. Normal would be the norm. Isn't it great to be so naïve?

Still, something was very, very wrong with my body. Still, something was very, very wrong with my brain. Still, I denied it very, very much. When I returned home with the medication for Anne, it began to subtly sink in that something had definitely happened. All I could say to Anne when I arrived at our house was that I had had some kind of "episode" in the pulpit. Deny, deny, and keep on denying. I still could not bring myself to say anything more than "episode" to the person whom I love and trust the most. Episode sounded so much more benign than the daunting words of what it really was. Deniability is so much better than facing reality; well, at the time it was.

I wrote down the following excerpts as a sort of firsthand account in another journal I was keeping at the time. They describe my first foray into the medical community of neurology. Though very subjective, they offer my rather naïve views that I would receive an immediate diagnosis and subsequently an alleviation of my condition. More importantly, they offer a glimpse at what many of us when first diagnosed want more than ever — to get back to normal.

My Primary Care Physician and I are on a first-name basis. His nurse took down a detailed account of my pharmacy measurement of blood pressure and pulse over the phone. Within an hour, I had an appointment for the next day. "Chip", my doctor's nickname and his nurse masterfully gathered medical data while all three of us very casually, or so I thought very casually, chatted. All the while, she was gathering medical information and jotting it down on his clipboard. My pulse and blood pressure had returned to normal. We might even be able to skip the blood pressure prescription medication. Blood was also taken to analyze. "Chip" did, nevertheless, order a CT Scan. He was now getting into the vicinity of the brain. We then made a token joke about my mind losing brain cells.

My Primary Care Physician contacted me later on to talk about reality gathered from the results of the tests. He went on to say that my carotid artery and heart were fine, but that there was a small spot on my brain that the

CT Scan picked up. "It's probably nothing," he said in an offhand voice, "but to err on the side of caution, I am referring you to a Neurosurgeon who can interpret the scan better than I can." "Okay," I said with a would-be-casual voice, "off the record what do you think it could be?" "The Neurosurgeon is in a better position to tell you that. I'm pushing hard to get you in to see him in a week. He usually has a three-month waiting list," my doctor added.

His tone was no longer nonchalant. Though he was still professional, my years of pastoral training were speaking to me that there was additional input to the situation. He was pushing to get me in and see a Neurosurgeon. "It's probably nothing," but he was, as I later found out, using his professional connections to get me in quicker to see a Neurosurgeon.

It was also during this time that the Neurosurgeon ordered an MRI to get a more in-depth medical picture of my brain than a CT scan could give. It was not too terrible going into a narrow closed-in tube with your head in a vise-type of object, though I had been warned by others who had undergone the procedure that it could be quite unsettling if you are the least bit claustrophobic. They offered me a Valium thirty minutes prior to putting me into the chute of leading-edge medical technology. Slowly shaking my head, I declined it. When the attendant wished me "good luck" as the process began, I second-guessed my refusal of the Valium.

I was encouraged that though I declined the Valium, what popped into my head was the Lord's Prayer. Over and over, I silently recited the traditional version that I had memorized from childhood and still prayed every Sunday in worship:

> Our Father, who art in heaven,
> hallowed be thy Name,
> thy kingdom come,
> thy will be done,
> on earth as it is in heaven.
> Give us this day our daily bread.
> And forgive us our trespasses,
> as we forgive those
> who trespass against us.
> And lead us not into temptation,
> but deliver us from evil.
> For thine is the kingdom,
> and the power, and the glory,
> for ever and ever. Amen.

I also snatched at and summoned certain scriptures seemingly out of the air that had also been put to memory. I was all alone. I was intimidated. If it was at all possible, though, I could hear the whispers of the Virgin Mary. *My soul magnifies the Lord, and my spirit rejoices in God my Saviour, for he has looked with favour on the lowliness of his servant.* — Luke 1:46

Any person who has ever been inside one of those claustrophobic torture chambers knows what the uncomfortable sensation is like. For those who don't, it is like being in an extremely narrow bunk bed with semi coffin-like curved walls on either side that meet in the middle to form a curved roof. There is a highly-sophisticated mirror that gives off a reverse telescope effect, which creates the illusion of more breathing space above your eyes and nose. In addition to this, the tech also gives you a pillow to put under your knees so, in their own words, "you'll be more comfortable."

It is exceptionally still and silent, semi-supernatural, that is, until the process begins. You can hear your frayed breathing and the palpable, balanced beating of your heart. Suddenly, a disconnected and disconcerting voice raids the machine. Instantaneously, the process begins. There are various eerie noises like whooshing interspersed with a blaring noise similar to those of the siren that comes from "The Emergency Broadcast System" while being blasted over the television.

In my case, there was also an unsettling reverberation that resembles hard carrots being rapidly chopped by a dull knife on a wooden cutting board. Carrots were not being chopped; instead, it was my brain — well, not really — that was being chopped up through Magnetic Resonance Imaging into an amazingly accurate picture for radiologists to read and then interpret the results to Neurologists and Neurosurgeons.

The Neurosurgeon called today to confirm my suspicion that there was something physiologically wrong in my brain. After reviewing the MRI, he was 100% sure that the spot on my brain was a Cavernous Malformation, which is akin to a noncancerous tumor. Even though it sounds so cliché, the time really did stand still when he called to deliver his diagnosis. It was right there in my garage on a warm, late-summer evening in September that straightforward medical information made my legs go icy and numb, while suddenly my forehead sported slippery sweat. I experienced a state of total detachment.

You cannot believe what you are hearing, but you know it to be a medical fact.

Psychologists would also classify this instant as a part of the process of grief with shock or denial being the first stage. I was prepared for the diagnosis, but stupidly and naively there was this fleeting thought of fantasy that this sort of thing only happens to "other people." I had become "other people." With that miniscule spot, I had crossed over the line and become a statistical stigma. George Choyce was added to a nonexistent list of very real people with a diagnosed Cavernous Malformation that brought on my condition.

Struggling for something to hang on to, I stammered something about medication to control my neurological situation. He responded rather nonchalantly, "Oh, I'll call you in a prescription called Keppra. It works very well." It was obvious to me, not only in that moment but also as I have reflected on the experience, that his professional yet detached voice mirrored verbatim discussions with hundreds, if not thousands of his patients. Though this may sound overly unsympathetic of what I call the "neuro-types of doctors," it is their professional responsibility to remain clinically detached in order to do their job. Even though he was not unkind, my preference would be for a bit more compassion. Compassion, however, is not his duty.

My Primary Care Physician had also referred me to a Neurologist to ensure that every neuro-type of doctor had a crack at examining me. It should be fairly obvious, but neurosurgeons perform surgery; neurologists don't. Neurologists propose ways via prescription to control neurological conditions.

Anne and I liked this particular Neurologist. He was professional yet very kind and understanding in the ways we had not experienced previously, though he admitted to never treating a clergyperson, especially one with my rare specific affliction. Shifting quickly on his stool, he became professionally inquisitive about the fact that the brain malady had manifested itself twice now when I was preaching. Probing further, he inquired, "Did you fall down? Did you lose consciousness? Did you wet yourself or lose control of your bowels?" "No. No. No," I responded to every single one of his questions, especially to that last question.

As he leaned forward in his stool, I could intuitively tell he was truly trying to understand my particular dilemma. He had treated all walks of life from crane operators to other doctors and almost everything else in between, so my confidence in him was not an issue. Finally, we were all getting a grip on this.

Chapter Eight

Overwhelmed

Humble yourselves before the Lord, and he will exalt you.
James 4:10

*O God, the source of all health: So fill my heart with faith in
your love, that with calm expectancy I may make room for
your power to possess me, and gracefully accept your healing;
through Jesus Christ our Lord. Amen.* BCP, p.461

"When was the last time it happened?" he
pressed on looking up from the notes he
was scribbling on his pad. "September
6th," came my instantaneous matter-of-fact reply. The
following is what I wrote in my journal that reflected on
that experience:

It was one of those Sundays that most clergy enjoy. It
was a low-key holiday weekend, but an above average
number of parishioners were in attendance to worship
anyway. Prior to the eleven o'clock service, I was relaxed
and joking with the Eucharistic Ministers, as well as
the two other priests. As we lined up for the procession,

and making double sure that my microphone was off, I pointed to my clergy collar and murmured in a kidding manner that there was a shocker in it and under the clergy seats there was a corresponding button. "Push the button if I fuzz out in the pulpit. It'll zap me out of my fuzz," I added with a smirk. The opening notes of the processional hymn sounded, and we processed on in with all the dignity we could muster after snickering. The liturgy had begun.

At the time of the sermon, confidently I settled myself into the pulpit beginning with the invocation "In the Name of the Father, and the Son, and the Holy Spirit." From that point on, I preached with a relish that often eludes the preacher. I was relaxed and enjoying proclaiming "Good News." The congregation was with me, and together we were all swept up together in the preaching experience. But something brought us back down with a pitiless thud.

Gazing up from about one-third of the way into delivering the sermon, shocked and anxious faces were staring back at me. Had I mispronounced a word that had come out a cuss word or unconsciously picked my nose up in the pulpit? Mulling these unpleasant scenarios over in my mind, quite suddenly I glanced over to the left to see a pharmacist from the congregation jumping up and jogging over promptly to the pulpit to join one of the clergy. I turned around and began to stammer over and over, "I'm okay." The Associate Rector said in a low voice, "Come down, George." She pulled on my hand which she later described as being as cold as ice. The pharmacist took a firm grip on my shoulder once I had clumsily navigated the steps of the pulpit and loudly stamped down onto the tile floor. He led me with an even firmer clasp down the side aisle into the Labyrinth Narthex. Another parishioner joined us and helped me sit down. The pharmacist looked at me and spoke:

Tell me your name.

Do you know where you are?

Count to ten.

"Hold both arms out," he firmly instructed me. I did what he said all the while wondering why he took me out of the service while I was preaching. I must get back in there to finish the sermon and assertively told him so. While thinking about this, the pharmacist began pushing down on both arms and asked me to push back up. These were all tests, I later discovered, to determine if I had had a mini stroke. Right then and there out in the Narthex, abruptly and without any pity, the gears ground together and clunked into place that another episode of fuzziness had just happened in the pulpit.

As I was driven home by the parishioner who had assisted the pharmacist out in the Narthex, I looked out the car window. My mind was perfectly clear, but there was no doubt that an octopus-like grip of inky darkness had its terrible tentacles around me strangling and squeezing light and life out of me. I had a medical condition that was more than physical. Whatever this condition of a Cavernous Malformation was, it was seeping its influence from my brain into the deepest part of my being — that place where no MRI or CT scan could reach — my spirit.

Now to get back to the very first appointment with my Neurologist: Looking at me square in the face, my Neurologist stated in a mechanically measured voice, "According to Tennessee Law, you cannot drive for six months. So that's March 6th for you." Rattled and overwhelmed, the stress-induced phenomenon of cottonmouth suddenly struck. My stress-induced, negative corporeal reaction vividly reminded me of my first meeting with the Bishop before going through the ordination process. In this case, I took a shot in the dark by asking in a hesitant, hoarse voice, "So what you're telling me is the doctor/patient privilege thing?" "No," he rapidly replied. "It's the law. If you had a car wreck and my records were subpoenaed, your insurance company would not cover you. It's not worth the risk because you could lose everything, everything."

I could tell that he, like the Neurosurgeon, had had these kinds of conversations with hundreds, if not thousands of his patients. There was a painful pause. In a steady, measured tone, my Neurologist stated quite clearly, "Mr. Choyce, you have epilepsy."

Chapter 9

It was Out

Jesus said to them, "Where is your faith?" Luke 8:25

Will you do your best to pattern your life in accordance with the teachings of Christ, so that you may be a wholesome example … ? BCP, p. 532

There was a silence that lasted for incalculable seconds, broken only by the back and forth squeaks of his stool. If you recall, the Bishop had also shifted his chair. There must be something about movement that is meant to minimize the bad news.

The Neurologist ordered one more test to confirm his diagnosis of epilepsy. It is an examination to measure brain waves called an EEG. On the day of the assessment, I was to lie down in a hospital bed, have uncomfortable electrodes pressed down at precise points on my scalp and then simply try to relax as a medically-complex machine measured my brain waves. I relaxed so much that I was snoring during the EEG, the tech informed me, at the end of the test.

The results came back. No doubt about it. The brain waves clearly indicated seizure activity.

As Anne and I walked out of his office to the parking lot, palpable and painful grief accompanied me every stride of the way. In the stages of grief, I was somewhere between denial and anger. Anger was winning at the moment. Handing the keys off to Anne, she asked, "What's this for? Oh, right," she said as an agonizing expression of comprehension dawned on her face. She had answered her own question. I opened the driver's side car door of my car for her. It was sad.

Sadness still did not keep stroke, stress, and exhaustion twirling through my mind as plausible explanations for seizures. Some in the congregation may have agreed with that compound diagnoses from this amateur neurological juggler. The brain condition of a Cavernous Malformation was not the culprit, I feebly contemplated. Seizure or epilepsy never occurred to me to say out loud. Every time I have had a seizure since my first one, the recurring knee-jerk reaction of denial follows. To whisper or even to scream, "That did not just happen," did not diminish the power of the seizures over me, however. So I employed a strategy of silence over my enemy of epilepsy. If I did not think the word seizure, then my epilepsy would stop and no longer have sway over me. How amazingly absurd! This strategy was designed to quite literally "put it out of my mind." It was all part of a pathetic plan that rather obviously did not work.

I am fully aware that this strategy is utterly illogical. You may be thinking stronger and more negative words than "illogical," and I do not blame you at all. What my brain rationalized is that if I do not think or speak about epilepsy anymore, then the epilepsy producing portion of my brain would not produce another seizure. This is denial to the nth degree. I want you to comprehend that this is the uncanny torment of seizures. Writing it over and over gives you a glimpse into the psyche of one who is authentically caught in the "Deny" phase of grief.

While deny, deny, deny may be a strategy in a Court of Law, the denial ploy did not work in my own court of life if there is such a thing. My brain kept betraying itself time and time again. My delusional world of control was unraveling in front of me and others. Though the seizures did not stop, at least what I had been referring to as "it" was no longer a secret.

Chapter Ten

Nonsensical Seizures

With many dreams come vanities and a multitude of words; but fear God. Ecclesiastes 5:7

O heavenly Father, who hast filled the world with beauty: Open our eyes to behold thy gracious hand in all thy works; that, rejoicing in thy whole creation, we may learn to serve thee with gladness; for the sake of him through whom all things were made, thy Son Jesus Christ our Lord. Amen. BCP, p. 814

Most of my seizures have transpired outside while simply running. Compare this scenario to that of the Down Syndrome young man. Awkwardly, he walks with his shoulders swinging back and forth with feet slapping on the cement through the neighborhood streets on his repetitive stroll. "Adorable" is the word repeatedly used to describe him.

Not me. To put it mildly, it is absolutely unsettling to be out running through Signal Mountain neighborhoods and not retain the memory of a particular portion of the run. It is an unnerving incident of missing time that the seizure has stolen. Picture this: These neighborhoods are the benign, almost bucolic, somewhat predictable places where kids are playing in front yards, dogs are barking behind their electric fences and parents are doing yard work or more likely, paying some yard service to do it for them.

Here is the part where it gets like a restless dream. As you run through this setting, you abruptly find yourself on a different part of the street. You can also find yourself stopped at one spot — staring at something or nothing at all — for no clear-cut rationale. You have utterly no recollection of how you arrived at that specific spot on the street. You question why you are staring at something or nothing in particular. A slight pressure behind your eyes subsides. You feel sick both physically and emotionally as your brain rushes to recover because this post-seizure time is often an instance of rampant, conflicting sensations. You wonder if anyone was watching you; paranoia penetrates your psyche. You are self-conscious even though there is no coherent reason to be mortified. After all, epilepsy is medical. A seizure is a medical incident. Saddest of all, you have bought into the sham and shame of the stigma of others who see you as an embarrassment.

I wish it was the "runner's high" that got me there to another spot on the street. A "runner's high" is one of those rare happenings when the runner is seemingly and painlessly transported to a different part of the street, track, or trail and has no lucid memory of how they got there. It is a pleasant experience — a natural high of a spike of endorphins in the brain with no effort associated with the experience.

Having a seizure while running, on the other hand, is the complete opposite. Contrary to a spike of endorphins, there is a misfiring of neurons. There is just no other way for me to describe it — it is unmistakably uncanny. I would ask myself in speedy succession, "Where am I? What in the world just happened? Why am I just staring into the woods? Where did the time go?" It may take a couple of seconds when you shake your head as if to clear it, then you carry on with your routine run and say over and over in an agitated sort of way, "That didn't just happen."

In addition to this, having a seizure while running is a manic experience. To someone in the denial phase of epilepsy, however, it is the only reality we can create in the brains that betray us in order for our world to make sense. We are frantic to frame some kind of reality out of our unreal world. Our world, a world that used to be fairly predictable is unraveling all around us. We want control, and our sense of command is stolen from us through one fickle seizure after another.

This next part of my seizure journey is nonsensical but must represent something of the mystique of the brain. When I have a seizure while running, my brain goes into an anesthetized, dream-like state. The dream I have is a recurring one and just plain peculiar. I do not know why, but in this state I am playing this game with my actual dogs named Oreo and Snickers. As a part of this game, a nameless, faceless foe is trying to catch my dogs. As a part of the game, my role is to direct the dogs out of harm's way. I am like a General in battle ordering the troops to strategic places on the battlefield. Oreo and Snickers, who are not there, run throughout the woods, and I direct them safely to me.

This is another layer of convolution to seizures. For whatever the medical reason is, my reoccurring seizures blend into the context of my location. It is an intermingling of part dream-like trance and part consciousness. This sounds absurd, but how much sense do your dreams make? When your brain betrays you, it is completely misfiring. In my neophyte understanding of epilepsy, the brain must be scrambling to make some sense out of the senseless situation. Do I need dream therapy to make sense of it all? There I go again. I want to make sense of the senseless; I want to control the monster that cannot be tamed. I make a feeble stab at humor to cope and deny. It's like trying to tame a lion with an unentertaining joke. It just will not succeed.

How I medically coped through denial even in the doctor's appointments that followed my seizures was my "go to" line of "not that I know of." As I pursued what I thought would be a quick cure, there were a number of paths taken. Neurologists and then Neurosurgeons — both local and at Vanderbilt — were to be a part of the mix that would get me back to "normal." When asked about seizures, I would fluently and honestly reply, "Not that I know of." This sounds very deceitful, but it is the partial truth if there is such a thing as partial truth.

The fact is that I could not swear that I had had a seizure if no one was there to verify it. That was my asterisks; that was my "I can neither confirm nor deny" legal line. For example, in the context of the run, I could have just stopped to catch my breath, felt dizzy and stared into the woods. I do not know why I would have done this. For all I know, my blood sugar could have been low. There is a slender prospect that it was not a seizure. I clung onto the frantic notion that nothing peculiar had happened. In retrospect, this is nothing more or less than a second-rate case of denial.

Chapter Ten

A Complex "Cure"

He sent forth his word and healed them and delivered them from their destruction. Psalm 107:20

May God the Father bless you, God the Son heal you, God the Holy Spirit give you strength. May God the holy and undivided Trinity guard your body, save your soul, and bring you safely to his heavenly country; where he lives and reigns for ever and ever. Amen. BCP, p. 460

The medical cure was not going to be a simplistic miracle. It came with its trade-offs. Twice a day at 8:30 in the morning and 8:30 at night, the alarm of my cell phone went off to remind me of what my children would shout out, "Drug time." I could take this amazing anti-seizure medication that would free me of seizures, but I had lost my driving privilege for six months from the date of my last seizure.

I could not stand the idea of being bound to a medication for the rest of my life, so at this time I began to pursue another option called Cyberknife. (See pages 204 - 208)

By the way, within weeks, I discovered I was allergic to Keppra. Keppra works well for most people, but I had developed a rare side effect known as the "Keppra Rash." To offset the rash, my Neurologist then put me on two other AEDs (antiepileptic drugs) called Lamotrigine and Vimpat; I found their side effects to be nasty.

There are many perks to being a parish priest. One such tailor-made perk for my situation is confidential counsel I receive from Physicians in the congregation. One such Doctor was a radiologist. He volunteered to read my MRI in order to render me his opinion, though this would be done strictly off the record. Coming over to my house on my day off, he put the disc in the computer and read the MRI in much greater detail. "There it is. There's the spot. That's the Cavernous Malformation," he called while pointing his finger at the computer screen. "So," I said crossly as a follow-up to the conversation, "my options to get rid of that thing are good old-fashioned crack-my-skull-open surgery or drugs to control the seizures. Great. Just great." I finished my sentence in a lame voice and sarcastic tone.

He leaned in and said with a smirk, "There are other options. Ever heard of Cyberknife?" Correctly reading Anne and my baffled stares, he plunged on, "It is an innovative process where radiation beams are precisely directed into your brain in order to destroy the Cavernous Malformation. Call The Cyberknife Center of Birmingham."

Hope. Hope is absolutely amazing. Probably if the technicians were to measure my brain waves with an EEG, at that point they would have changed to spell out the word H O P E.

Chapter Eleven

The Cyberknife "Cure"

O Lord my God, I cried to you for help, and you healed me.
Psalm 30:2

*Almighty God our heavenly Father, graciously comfort your
servant George in his suffering, and bless the means made
use of for his cure. Fill his heart with confidence, that though
at times he may be afraid, he yet may put his trust in you;
through Jesus Christ our Lord. Amen.* P. 459 BCP

I t was time to get stern and compose a plan to pursue
as much information as I could about Cyberknife.
Tennessee had all but a handful of Cyberknife
Centers at that time. Probably out of some sense of
gratuitous loyalty to the state of Tennessee over the
next week, I contacted two of the Tennessee hospitals
that had a Cyberknife Center. After my records had
been sent to Knoxville, the University of Tennessee said
that I was not a candidate for Cyberknife. In addition
to this disillusionment, Vanderbilt in Nashville could get
me in, but it would take some time even to get my first
appointment to discuss the prospect of Cyberknife as a

treatment for the Cavernous Malformation. At this point, I felt that the microscopic one centimeter Cavernous Malformation had expanded blocking all the roads to recovery. The miniscule Cavernous Malformation was taking over all 170 pounds of me and mocking all of my serious stabs to resolve this medical condition.

At this point, there was nothing to lose. I contacted The Cyberknife Center of Birmingham. They could get me in, in just two weeks. Why had I been faithful to Tennessee?

When you are desperate, you hear what you want to hear. I did not want to hear that Cyberknife was not a quick cure for my seizures; nevertheless, I went forward to have precisely-focused lasers of radiation, instead of a scalpel, penetrate deeply into the left frontal region of my brain. It works in theory. Is it going to work in reality?

Anne and I drove, rather she drove, and I rode and met with a Neurosurgeon that used Cyberknife. He sat down with both of us. He said intently, "Listen, I want to know what is going on here. I want to get a sense of who you both are and how this condition is affecting your lives." Anne and I were able to recount the seizures and the fact that it was truly beginning to intrude on our lives, our kids' lives, and what it meant to be a priest who had to deal with seizures in such a public way. The Doctor was deeply sympathetic.

"I see how being a priest with seizures could be very problematic, although I've never had your specific situation before," he said quite candidly. "So we're going to do something about this, but not today or tomorrow. We're going to go slow to get it right, but we will get it. I assure you that I have had much, much worse. Look, this affects your life. So I'm going to get it," he assured Anne and me with a determined and confident look in his eyes.

He led us out into the hallway and put the results of my latest MRI (he had ordered the MRI earlier that day) up on a screen. "There it is," he piped up as he pointed to a clearly visible spot on my brain. "You got a healthy brain except for that one spot," he added. "What's that dark area around the spot?" Anne inquired. "Blood. That's where it's hemorrhaged. That's why we have got to get it," he stated with an authority in his voice that gave Anne and me complete confidence. "Then let's do this," I exclaimed. All three of us beamed.

Afterwards, I found out that the insurance company "needed more information" about Cyberknife surgery. The Neurosurgeon's office was immediately on it and assertively responded to the insurance company's "need for more information" by giving it to them. I was approved for surgery and eager to get on with my life. If I had made it this far, then surely Cyberknife would be the solution to my seizures.

The day of the Cyberknife surgery was finally here. "The size of your Cavernous Malformation is so small this will only take thirty minutes. When it's over, you won't even believe anything has happened," explained the tech. I listened to some Taize (a sort of modern chant) music during the procedure. A form-fitted, mesh mask was then placed over my head to keep me immobile as possible during the Cyberknife Surgery. A machine arm that is about twice the size of one of those x-ray machines at a dentist's office moved all around my head as the surgery began and continued this type of movement throughout the operation. Thirty minutes later, it was over. It was painless. Anne drove me home.

Chapter Twelve

Christmas Eve Epilepsy

Hope deferred makes the heart sick ... Proverbs 13:12

But the angel said to them, "Do not be afraid; for see—I am bringing you good news of great joy for all the people..." Luke 2:10

Father, you loved the world so much that in the fullness of time you sent your only Son to be our Savior. Incarnate by the Holy Spirit, born of the Virgin Mary, he lived as one of us, yet without sin. To the poor he proclaimed the good news of salvation; to prisoners, freedom, to the sorrowful, joy ... BCP, p. 374

Christmas Eve — the date when most Churches around the country fill up with not only "all ye faithful" but with the C and E crowd which does not mean Church of England but rather Christmas and Easter Christians.

The regulars, the not-so-regulars, and even many visitors were there. And they were happy. They were smiling. Perhaps this recession was beginning to break, and people had something to look forward to for 2010. Perhaps they, like little children, still believed that something unbelievable, something miraculous could come to pass at Christmas. And perhaps the story of God becoming human in the infant Jesus does have a mysterious, immeasurable effect on all of our lives. As I have written earlier, hope is miraculous.

On this Christmas Eve, the Altar Guild once again outdid itself. The members of the Altar Guild had decorated the Nave, Chapel, and Narthex in the true Episcopal style of tasteful yet understated. What's more, candles were precisely positioned giving off the faint glow that only natural light can offer. For me, flame flickering candles have always pointed towards a luminescent holiness that is both transcendent and immanent. This beautiful blinking, nevertheless, is a promoter for seizures. Also, the Holy Family was behind the Altar on the front shelf contained in a crèche surrounded by gorgeous greenery and more candles. The stringed instruments accompanied the choir in an eclectic mix ranging from a Chinese Christmas Carol sung by the children to "Oh Holy Night" stunningly vocalized by an opera singer. Also, a tasteful scent of incense infused the air with a heavenly aroma.

To say that I was psyched would be an understatement; the adrenaline was pumping. Regrettably for me, stress, even pleasant tension, is another catalyst for seizures. Everything was combining in such a way that every person coming to worship on this Christmas Eve would be moved all the way to the unfathomable part of their soul. They would be touched by all of the sensory input from the sight of the decoration, the sound of the music, and the scent of the incense.

It is usually both a privilege and responsibility of the rector to preach on Christmas Eve. This was a sermon I had been preparing for at least two weeks which, in and of itself, is more time than most clergy have for regular sermon preparation period. I had gone over it again and again and knew that this one was "a keeper."

It was fun preaching that night. The congregation needs to see a priest who enjoys preaching and is having fun while preaching. Fun does not mean silliness or gimmicky. People like to see other people doing something that they enjoy. Why should preaching be any different? When you hear a nervous preacher, this nervousness cannot help but spread to the congregation. The opposite, of course, is true. A joyful preacher spreads joy.

The congregation knew what I had been through since early August. They also knew about my recent Cyberknife surgery. This was the triumph we all shared. Could there be a more appropriate time to share in it than on the night that we celebrated that birth of Christ?

I stepped into the pulpit around 11:20 that night. The adrenaline was compensating for my exhaustion. For me, nonetheless, lack of sleep was another facilitator for seizures. The adrenaline was winning because I felt good, and I felt good about delivering the Good News on Christmas Eve of God's love for all of us who had been broken over the past year. These reflections pleasantly plunged me into a more insightful level of faith. Though I had frequently preached about the miracle of healing in the framework of Christmas Eve sermons, this particular Christmas Eve sermon would have more authenticity. I had been healed. I had especially been healed of seizures. It was a community celebration.

As I started the sermon, my eye contact with the congregation was especially personal. I could see their faces in subdued illumination, and it was just like I was preaching to each person as an individual. Still, I had entered the pulpit with my "unholy trinity" of flickering lights, adrenaline, and exhaustion for company. About four minutes into the sermon, I observed that five rows from the pulpit there was a visiting family with a small girl of perhaps three years of age squirming in the alternating laps of her mother and then her father after 11 o'clock. By the time of the sermon, they had given up on keeping their daughter still. What's the harm, they must have thought, of just letting little "so and so" twirl noiselessly in the dim, distant side aisle during the sermon? And so she did. And many eyes traveled towards the little girl completely annoyed with such behavior in church. My eyes traveled to her, and that is the last thing I remember.

My arms grabbed the sides of the pulpit, locked in their position, pushed the rest of my body up as if exercising as my legs uncontrollably rocked back and forth. Within ten seconds, the Associate Rector and a Eucharistic Minister were talking to me and lightly pulling me down from the pulpit. The Eucharistic Minister and another parishioner walked me out of the Nave because I found out later that my legs were uncoordinated and my feet were stomping.

Once in my office, the hodgepodge of tones made no sense, but I felt my lavaliere microphone being vigorously plucked away from my alb. It felt like waking up from a dream of disconnected male and female voices, even though I was sitting up in a chair in my office. Two Doctors from the congregation were standing over me and one stated in both a professional and pastoral voice, "George, you just had a seizure." Looking at her in disbelief, I blurted out, "But I have to get back in there and finish the sermon." "The only place you're going is home," she stated through gritted teeth in a voice of authority that plainly told me not to argue with her.

Being driven home on Christmas Eve before the service was even halfway over by one of the parishioners who had helped to escort me out of church was perhaps one of the lowest moments in my vocation as a priest. Oh yes, the clerical collar was literally shaken by another seizure. I was helpless over my condition, even after the surgery that was supposed to cure me. Epilepsy had rendered me so powerless that I would not even be allowed back into the Nave to finish up the sermon or celebrate the Eucharist on Christmas Eve. The Doctors had ordered me home. Where was God in all of this?

It was the first Christmas Eve I had not celebrated in eighteen years. What a horrible thing to put the congregation through again. What a horrible thing the Associate Rector had to go through as she again put on her "game face" by immediately picking up the service — Christmas Eve of all times — at the Nicene Creed. What a horrible thing to put Anne through again as I walked into the kitchen at 11:45, and she moaned, "You're home early ... Oh, no." She knew instantaneously what had come to pass.

Chapter Thirteen

Hints that Leave Me Nowhere to Hide

Surely, it is God who saves me; I will trust in him and not be afraid. Isaiah 12:2 RSV

Come to me, all you that are weary and are carrying heavy burdens, and I will give you rest. Matthew 11:28

Assist us mercifully, O Lord, in these our supplications and prayers, and dispose the way of thy servants towards the attainment of everlasting salvation; that, among all the changes and chances of this mortal life, they may ever be defended by thy gracious and ready help; through Jesus Christ our Lord. Amen. BCP, p. 832

I was talking with a nurse at that reception when my last seizure silently struck. It transpired with no warning at all. Some with epilepsy have an aura, which is a semi-warning system that a seizure is upcoming; the seizure is either imminent or hours away. Furthermore, auras vary significantly from person to person. For instance, an aura may ensue right before a seizure or several minutes to hours earlier. Some with epilepsy are grateful for the warning that an aura creates, while others dread them because the sensation an aura produces is unpleasant in and of itself, not to mention the mental torture of the certainty of the seizure that is surely to come. Common warning signs right before seizures are changes in bodily sensations, changes in your ability to interact with things happening outside you, and changes in how familiar the outside world seems to you. Other commonly recognized warning signs that may happen hours before a seizure are depression, irritability, sleep disruption, nausea, and headache.

As the English would say, I finally had "plucked up the courage" to call the nurse two weeks after the previous seizure and requested of her to recall the events. Here is what I frantically scribbled down on a piece of notebook paper regarding that discussion:

(We were having an) Enjoyable conversation about my mother

(You) Shut down

(You) Looked away

(She) Kept conversation going not to draw attention to what was going on

(You) Looked around

(You) Moved hands as if you did not know what to do with them

(Your) Jaw dropped

Others around us knew what was happening and joined in the conversation so as not to draw attention to what was happening

(We) Took you by hand through the kitchen

(We) Sat you in a chair outside

You "came to."

All I remember was being led through the kitchen with shoes slapping the floor in a surreal state of slow motion, while appalled faces looked on as I was being seated in a chair outside like some sort of naughty kid. By this time others had noticed, especially Anne and two of our children. There was no "not that I know of" excuse I could give, which was always my line when visiting the doctors.

This is just one portion of the terrible psychological power that a person living with seizures senses. To use an example from nature, the talons of the scrounging vulture of seizures have penetrated every attempt you have made to ward off the foul, parasite-infested bird. You are tainted by the angst of a medical condition you cannot control.

Simply put, I felt contaminated. It is the sociology of fear that society has projected on you, and now the fear has taken up residence in your consciousness. The virus of fear has begun to grow and mutate, mutate and grow. Epilepsy had become anxiety incarnate. There was no more denial; there was no more delusion. This last seizure was more than the congregation could cope with so I went on medical disability.

Chapter Fourteen

STAGE II — ANGER

The Cauldron Simmers

Do not be quick to anger, for anger lodges in the bosom of fools. — Ecclesiastes 7:9

Rend your hearts and not your clothing. Return to the Lord, your God, for he is gracious and merciful, slow to anger, and abounding in steadfast love, and relents from punishing. Joel 2:13

O merciful Father, who hast taught us in thy holy Word that thou dost not willingly afflict or grieve the children of men: Look with pity upon the sorrows of thy servant for whom our prayers are offered. Remember him, O Lord, in mercy, nourish his soul with patience, comfort him with a sense of thy goodness, lift up thy countenance upon him, and give him peace; through Jesus Christ our Lord. Amen. BCP, p. 831

The following journal entry is a fitting lead-in to the anger phase of grief. It helped me cope with my grief on the day I wrote it, knowing that someone else someday would read it in the context of this journal.

By vocation, I am an Episcopal Priest. My "holy" vocation, however, did not bring to a halt what happened deep within the left frontal lobe of my brain; in fact, it might have even caused it. Physiologically, what happened at about eleven o'clock the morning of August 2 was an explosion of sorts — an explosion of blood. For whatever reason, an abnormal cluster of nerves in my brain called a Cavernous Malformation, violently forced blood out in all directions. Under immense pressure, blood splattered throughout a miniscule area of my brain. In other words, deep within my left frontal lobe a tiny area under extreme force pressed outward in all directions resulting in a brain hemorrhage.

The internal bleeding irritated a small section of tissue in my brain, and the neurons in my nervous system misfired and resulted in a seizure. (See page 204) The specific classification of my seizure is called a complex partial seizure. (See page 196-197) My complex partial seizure, regrettably, took place in the context of a sermon. Some parishioners thought I was pausing for almost two minutes for dramatic effect. No one, except for my associate, talked about the "episode" to me after the service. The subject of seizures is still taboo, even in the twenty-first century.

The word "seizure" is recognizable to most of us. My guess is that most of you reading this picture a seizure in the framework of someone falling down, becoming rigid and shaking uncontrollably. I limited my understanding of a seizure that way before August 2, 2009. My epilepsy journey has led me to the coherent comprehension that there is a wide range regarding the classification of seizures. There are seizures that run a gamut of simple to complex, brief to long, standing to falling.

In my opinion, and at the risk of sounding rather preachy, we must move past ignorance concerning seizures. It is significant for you to know the medical classifications and descriptions of seizures, which are at the end of this book. Most people recognize the terms "petit mal" and "grand mal," yet these classifications are outmoded and imprecise. (See pages 196-198 for a more complete list.) In addition to this, having an elementary grasp of seizures can remarkably reduce the phobia of seizures.

I should know since people started to avoid me after finding out about my epilepsy as if I were infectious or would "go off" in front of their children or grandchildren. Furthermore, if I were to have a seizure in public, I would embarrass them in public. (This phenomenon is not, by any means, unique to me. Many with epilepsy feel this way.) What makes this so psychologically painful is that some of these people were my friends, key word here being "were." Betrayal and abandonment are not hard-hitting enough words to describe my feelings. As emotional as these feelings are, they are part and parcel of the indispensable steps of the grieving process.

It is not, however, epilepsy alone that evokes these strong passions. Other neurological conditions, from the **A** of ALS (known as Lou Gehrig's disease) to the **Z** of Zellweger Syndrome, have some sick stigma attached to them which only serves to magnify the physical pain and emotional turmoil of the medical condition. For instance, it was only after an article of mine was published (see pages 200-203) concerning my new life with epilepsy and how I was desperately trying to regain my vocation as a priest that a colleague of mine wrote in a letter to me about Parkinson's disease what I had written about epilepsy. He too used the words embarrassment, as well as contagious. He too felt abandoned by friends, as well as colleagues. He too had people who did not know how to interact with him even on the surface level when he went public about his Parkinson's.

Can you believe this? Now for just a minute, I ask that you stretch your imaginations. I wonder how many of you have ever undergone this treatment in any type of situation. For those of you living with a disability, I need write no more on your feelings or experiences. That would be beneath patronizing.

For those of you who do not live with a disability, I honestly hope you can tap into an experience, any experience when you felt similar to my colleague with Parkinson's who must feel this way on a daily basis. Have you ever been treated as if you were contagious? Have you ever felt your very presence was an embarrassment? Have you ever been intimidated and anxious about going out in public to do something as simple as shopping? Envision never getting reprieve from the pessimistic way you are treated. I hope you are so ticked off right now that your passion in this anger phase of grief leads you to have a vision to do something about it. I think that this book is how I am responding positively to the passion of anger. The two of us are stronger than one of me.

For me, I ask that you give me something precious of yours — more of your time. It really is that simple, and it really is that hard. Case and point — I know I am slow. The high-powered medication I am on causes me to talk and walk sluggishly, as well as sometimes to even slur my words. Now and again, I stumble. I frequently forget names, as well as some subject we have just discussed. These are the quite common side effects of almost all anti-seizure medications. So is exhaustion. By the way, I have to drink two cups of coffee in the morning simply to function.

It all adds up to the illusion that I am intoxicated if I am unable to have my coffee. This is embarrassing to the onlooker. I wonder what you would think of me if you were that onlooker. What would you think of me if you met me on one of my bad medicine days: sluggish walk, slurred words, and stumbling? A drunken priest, really! It creates guilt by association.

Another case and point — a colleague of mine was on an even more powerful combination of anti-seizure medications for a different medical condition altogether, that he also, from time to time came across as inebriated. Just like my other clergy colleague with Parkinson's, this priest embarrassed them. As if in retaliation, the ultimate insult was to embarrass him by doing an intervention. And later, when it was proven that he did not have an issue with alcohol, his congregation continued to make it so difficult for him to stay on as their Rector that he took retirement disability just so that he would continue to get some form of stipend in order to take care of his family. He and his spouse no longer go to church ... anywhere; neither do his kids!

According to Dr. Elisabeth Kubler-Ross, anger is the second stage of the grief. Just as the loss of a loved one is a part of grief, the loss of health is just that — a loss, a loss of something significant in our lives. Loss is loss. Sudden loss of your health is something that others might not grasp as loss; however, when someone guides you by the hand and gently sits you into a chair as if you are a child learning to walk, and you have no memory of the last two minutes, you have not only experienced a seizure, you have experienced a loss. For me, it was not just a loss of health; it was also a loss of dignity. Emotionally, I had lost my self-respect.

"It's a medical condition," you may be thinking. "Why would you lose your self-respect?" you may be asking. For me, the losses were emotional and extremely personal. For me, the losses were my objective reality. I imagine that others who have seizures suffer something like I was feeling on that day, as well as the dull emotions associated with epilepsy in the years to come.

Chapter Fifteen

This Fool's Fight for Control

And I said: "Woe is me! I am lost ... !" Isaiah 6:5

Even though I walk through the darkest valley, I will fear no evil; for you are with me; your rod and your staff — they comfort me. Psalm 23:4

The Almighty Lord, who is a strong tower to all who put their trust in him, to whom all things in heaven, on earth, and under the earth bow and obey: Be now and evermore your defense, and make you know and feel that the only Name under heaven given for health and salvation is the Name of our Lord Jesus Christ. Amen. BCP, p. 456-457

B
oth sharp and dull emotions become reality to many of us with epilepsy, even though most of us know that our condition is medical. For instance, even to come up with a synonym for loss makes the reality of epilepsy that much more a cause for the emotion of anger to me. While writing this part of my epilepsy experience, I desperately searched for another word for "loss." My inquiry led me to more resentment toward

the word "loss." As I spent some time in reflection, the synonyms that plagued my brain exploded in alliteration — smash, smear, smack, slaughter. The synonyms transferred over to rhyme with the words defeat, beat, and then unseat. Pure and simple, I failed. As a guy, it kills my ego to know that epilepsy has beaten me. I have lost. George lost. George is a loser.

As ludicrous as it might sound, my brain beats itself up. It sabotages itself. My brain sucker-punched itself through a minuscule soft-spot of irritation; it sent the misfiring of brain waves to infiltrate the other microscopic parts of my brain and gave itself a TKO. Think of it this way — a one-centimeter remnant of a Cavernous Malformation and the three centimeters of the blood byproduct of iron that surrounded the Cavernous Malformation brought down the two to three pounds of the rest of my brain. No timeouts allowed here. No warning whatsoever. There was nothing I could do to stop the fight that was taking place in my very own skull. Neurons misfire; it is that simple and that complex. I cannot trust my brain. The trust is gone. It has betrayed me.

I began my last sermon at my former parish with the words from the first stanza of Simon and Garfunkel's song about a boxer. As dauntingly difficult as it was for me to go back to this sermon, it reflects a part of my injured soul. My physical battle had morphed into a spiritual battle, because it was now, like a virus, transmitting an infection into my sermons.

To return to the physical side of the skirmish, I am in a fight against this thing inside my head. This physical side of epilepsy, however, reminded me of a fascinating conversation I had with a pharmacist friend of mine who began, "Anything from the neck up is like the universe. There is so much we do not know. There is so much to explore." "Oh just great, just great," I mumbled almost inaudibly while looking down at my feet concerning his straightforward yet distressing pronouncement.

For me, the physical side of epileptic seizures had already transformed into an emotional side of a struggle. This fighting mentality has served me well but only to a certain extent. The psychological clash gave me the courage to endure complex neurosurgery to remove the entire area of irritation. People have said that they both envied and admired my guts to "go under the knife," especially to have my scalp, skull, and brain invaded by a precision surgical scalpel to remove an infinitesimal portion of tissue.

But there is a downside. From my perspective, seeing seizures as a fight is unhealthy for my soul, too. If almost everything is a fight throughout this whole experience, the walls go up in order to be insulated from being hurt. My anger is really a morphing of fear. Fear, I have constantly preached, is the opposite of faith. It shuts us down. It was shutting me down. I was shutting God out because of my fear. And that was extraordinarily revealing of my spiritual state. For instance, "There is no fear in love, but perfect love casts out all fear; for fear has to do with punishment ..." I John 4:18. This priest's faith was, beyond a doubt, stirred. Was that going to turn out a good thing for my wounded self?

I have done my soul searching with this question - Did this preacher ever really believe any of his sermons? For now, I want to believe. Has my faith been so shaken, like my clerical collar, that it has brought me to the precipice of whether or not I believe in God anymore? Believing in God makes me too vulnerable. What is the alternative? This guy wants to be in charge of change. God, this is so hard! At the very least, I am crying out to God that this is so hard.

I want to shelter myself behind the walls of isolation because I am scared. I am not really living but merely existing. My emotions are going to be so protected, but then the paradox is that my epilepsy has "won." And there I go again with winning and losing.

Chapter Sixteen

Epilepsy is Driving Me Crazy

My spirit is broken ... Job 17:1

For everything there is a season, and a time for every matter under heaven: Ecclesiastes 3:1

Comfort and heal all those who suffer in body, mind, or spirit; give them courage and hope in their troubles, and bring them the joy of your salvation. BCP, p. 389

Lord, in your mercy
Hear our prayer. BCP, p. 389

With seizures comes another loss for some of us. It is the loss of driving. Let me ask you, "Can you still go almost anywhere you want to go seemingly whenever you want to do so?" For someone with epilepsy, mobility is a day-to-day, often humdrum, occasionally an undignified begging, and sometimes a frantic coordination conundrum. For instance, this afternoon a friend is taking my son and me to the orthopedic surgeon to have a permanent cast put on his wrist because he fractured it while roller skating.

Emanating from my son's accident while roller skating, comes my metaphorical emotional roller coaster of always having to coordinate my schedule in order to get a ride from someone. Stemming from simply out-of-thin-air is a taunting voice that malevolently whispers, "You cannot even take care of your youngest son. Ha."

"It makes me so sick to my stomach not being able to drive." I actually emailed that sentence to a woman who had lost her driving privilege to seizures. I was thinking much worse but did not put pen to paper to describe it. Upon reflection, I have emailed some form of being sick or nauseated or vomiting to more and more people living with epilepsy who are beginning to contact me about the experience apropos to the loss of my driving privilege. It is just dreadful because you are dependent on someone else. It's humbling. Again, as a guy who is now 51, this dependency is another blow to my ego, my sense of self-worth. I am getting older and not aging well.

What's more, living with epilepsy means that other people live with my epilepsy. One small centimeter has affected so many in scores of significant ways. So "Why," you might inquire, "could not your spouse or children or friends chauffeur you around?" The simple response is that your spouse or children or friends have their own lives to lead. They cannot be expected to drive you around all the time, even when it comes to your own kids. They might have the only job, and the money they make is critical to the running of the household. They might have other doctors' appointments to attend, including their own. They might have school — Graduate, Undergraduate, or High School. These phases of school are exactly where the Choyce children are right now.

Life does not come to a standstill for everyone else just because you are living with epilepsy. My world is not everyone else's world. Even sincere friends and family who say, "Call me anytime if you need a ride, even if it is at midnight," have their own lives to lead. You get resentful. Many promises of coming by and taking me to lunch have been broken. The resentfulness increases almost to a rage.

I wrote the following in another journal back in 2010:

As a part of my healing process, some of the time off was used to go to the beach and go fishing. Nothing to me is more healing than being on the beach going fishing with my family. This time, however, I was going without my immediate family except for the fact that I was catching a ride with my parents and being completely dependent upon them for most of my mobility excluding walking. There were glimpses of déjà vu during the trip. "Mom, can you come pick me up?", and "Dad, would you be able to drive me to the store?" Thirty-two years ago, I requested these things of them when I was in high school.

From my perspective, anger is fed by a restless isolation from others. If there is such a thing, you have too much time to reflect upon your circumstances. You are so close to borderline narcissism because the epilepsy experience forces and focuses the attention on yourself. It is not like, at least for me, physical incarceration. But it is close.

The word "prisoner," when it comes to epileptic isolation, is cliché. It is also inaccurate. I can get out, weather permitting, and go on a walk or a run. I can get out of the house, yet the quandary still lies with the social seclusion from other people. Though it sounds incredibly insensitive, at the very least, prisoners are not isolated from one another unless they are in Solitary Confinement.

What is more, since I am an introvert, this notion of having time unaccompanied used to appeal to me. Now, even so, it would be pleasant to exercise my less frequent extroverted side for some small dollops of time. A telephone call, email, or texts are some forms of "technical touch," and even they would be a welcome distraction from my segregation from others.

I was agitatedly reflecting on this very thing yesterday while nervously striding back and forth and gazing up at the sky, all the while taking my frustration out on the Lord and panting out loud with the plea, "Just tell them to give me a call, even if it is only a token greeting." And this was at one of the most relaxing places to me — the beach at St. Simons Island in Georgia. It must have looked pathetic, perhaps even creepy to those who were involuntarily eavesdropping. Being confined due to seizures must be like a torture to the extroverted. The effect of the torment was even manifesting itself in the introverts; well, it was now coming out in this particular introvert named George.

For me, the overcast, dreary days become claustrophobic. Perhaps my experience comes across as whiny or self-absorbed or even self-pitying. From what I have experienced in just a little over two and a half years, my head continues to mock my situation. The same scornful voice that previously and sarcastically mocked, "Don't have a seizure," is now saying, "You don't have a job. You're not doing anything." Since my internal narrator emanates from the same place where you keep your brain, the demented derision is double.

Chapter Seventeen

Something About Misery and Company

When you are disturbed, do not sin; ponder it on your beds, and be silent. Psalm 4:4

Do not harden your hearts ... as when your ancestors tested me. Psalm 95:8a,9a

We thank you also for those disappointments and failures that lead us to acknowledge our dependence on you alone. BCP, p. 836

I
t is in these painful places and times, though, that often a close connection can be forged with others who have seizures. There is a profound bond that often develops among those with epilepsy, even though our experiences are not in complete correspondence. For example, recently I met a man and his spouse at an Episcopal Convention, which reinforced the preceding phenomenon. They specifically sought me out after being informed that I have seizures. Why there was an immediate connection between the three of us, I really

do not know other than it must have been the mysterious and medical tie formed through the common experience of seizures.

Our experience with different categories of seizures was profoundly poles apart, however. This particular man would have what is known as a simple partial seizure — a time when he would stare; that category of seizure would be followed by a seizure categorized as tonic-clonic — falling to the ground followed by jerking movements. The simple partial seizure was the "canary in the coal mine" and gave them the forewarning that it was time to go to the hospital.

As is often the case with epilepsy, there are intricate emotional issues surrounding a seizure. They were upset about this whole scenario, not only that it had happened, but it had happened after six years of being seizure-free. Since December 2011 to January 2012, he had three seizures within a six-week timeframe. That feeling of helplessness was palpable in the midst of the conversation. You think you're free of epilepsy and then the seizures sneak up on you and pounce. The illusion of control is once again shattered; nevertheless, it was healing for them to share it with me. Moreover, it was healing for me to listen.

This illusion of control continues to be a common thread with those who thought they had suppressed their seizures for good. It was disheartening to hear the following stories:

One person lost his job in the medical equipment industry and is on disability. He could not afford to have a seizure in the operating room, nor could his patient for that matter.

Another doctor went from high-risk surgery in obstetrics to a medical family practice. The medical story is the same — he could not afford to have a seizure in the operating room, nor could his patients.

The third person had to cut back on her work schedule as a television personality in which she excelled. She also had to resign from the Epilepsy Foundation due to the amount of work it required.

These three had seizures while they were on the job.

Furthermore, not one of these three was happy about receiving disability payments or reducing their workload. I write this because some might think that epilepsy would be the perfect alibi to live on disability or to reduce one's workload. It was not the case with them nor is it with me. Though our workload was eliminated or reduced, we are all working through our epilepsy — a tedious and trying job that never ends. I am not sorry if any of this comes across as preachy. It is quite candid sore stuff that needs to come out. It is reality. It hurts. Quite frankly, and to drastically tame my keyboard here, all I can gracefully write is that it makes me mad; really mad.

As an interesting aside, for two suffering with seizures with whom I have met, their seizures were first manifested in childhood. One had a teacher who knew something medical was going on. The other had a teacher who thought that she was faking seizures to get out of class. I honestly understand the second teacher's point of view, but this is part and parcel of the pattern of what an epileptic person, in this case even a child, must endure. Put yourself in the place of that child or the child's parent or parents for that matter, whose teacher thought she was faking a seizure to get out of class. What are you feeling right now? Are you mad? Mad at all? Really, really mad? Welcome to our world.

I have already written about the sturdy bond that develops between those living with epilepsy. Imagine then what happens when you discover someone who is in your same vocation or had a similar life experience. This is what finally transpired in February of 2013. I discovered the name of a pastor with epilepsy, who is retired and currently living in Florida. He had three tonic-clonic seizures roughly eight years apart while serving at different parishes. He said to me proudly, "All three of my parishes surrounded me with love and support, and that is why I stayed on with them. For me, it was the Christian community living out the words 'see how they love one another.'" He was referring to the words that church historian Tertullian recorded in the third century of what the pagans said when referring to the Christians.

This is my journal, though millions of others' lives write it with me. Thus far you have been given a verbal snapshot of my epilepsy pilgrimage, yet this section of my journal is far more expansive than George Choyce's seizures. I am one of approximately two to three million suffering with seizures in the United States; hence, I have intentionally included others with epilepsy in this portion of my journal. My story is too constricted in focus if it does not bring in others who suffer from seizures. Our diverse experiences are a kind of cumulative epilepsy journal with a broader and clearer picture than my synoptic image. Our diversity is held together with the delicate strand of having at least two seizures, which is the medical definition of epilepsy.

Our stories impart stronger voice to a medical condition, one that is still scary and terribly taboo. Our accounts bestow clearer eyes to the reader about those with epilepsy whom you will probably never see because the severity of their seizures keeps them out of sight from the mainstream. Those with multiple, uncontrolled seizures throughout the day, whose seizures are unresponsive either to surgery or anticonvulsants or both, leave them true captives to this medical condition called epilepsy. They are human, and they are hidden.

Chapter Eighteen

Go Ahead; You Try It

But if you are angry with a brother or sister, you will be liable to judgment ... Matthews 5:22

Be reconciled to your brother or sister... Matthew 5:24

May almighty God in mercy receive your confession of sorrow and of faith, strengthen you in all goodness, and by the power of the Holy Spirit keep you in eternal life. Amen. BCP, p. 451

I want you to visualize having the following category of seizure throughout the day and what you would feel like subsequent to each attack. Your body shakes, and then you cannot control your movements. You get an intense, completely involuntarily, whole body workout. Some of the time, you lose control of your bladder and/or your bowel. You are nauseous. And to top it all off, you do not even remember having the seizure! You just know that you have had a seizure, and some people suppose that you are not trying hard enough to rid yourself of these episodes. Again, welcome to our world. To be even more specific, welcome to my world because the exact experiences have occurred now more than once to me.

Here is a comparison that will be helpful in understanding what those with daily, multiple tonic-clonic, otherwise known as grand mal, seizures must endure: Some people I have talked with, who even disclose to having a tonic-clonic seizure on a sporadic basis, have said to me that they usually have to rest for twenty-four to thirty-six hours to regain their full strength. I cannot grasp what this must be like for the invisible ones with multiple, daily tonic-clonic seizures. Can you?

Now imagine consenting to someone caring for you when you shower, bathe, dress or go to the bathroom because you have numerous tonic-clonic seizures throughout the day, each and every day. You simply cannot live on your own. It could be lethal. While I may live on my own for now, my Neurologist has instructed me not to take a bath alone in case I have a seizure. The water would not wake me up. I would drown. He has even gone so far out of professional concern for me to boldly state, "I can't tell you not to take a shower, but you need to use caution." Please pause for a minute or two now and reflect on how seizures would impinge on your basic, everyday life.

This is not new to those, like me, with epilepsy. We are like Prince John (12 July 1905 — 18 January 1919), in that we are sent away and concealed from sight. In his case, Prince John of England was sequestered at a family farm in the country because he was an embarrassment to the Royal Family. Does the word "embarrassment" sound recognizable? Today's "Prince Johns" are the invisible people with epilepsy who dwell, hardly ever on bucolic family farms, but behind the walls of houses, apartments, townhouses or trailers or are permanently confined to a medical-type of facility.

Though this is my journey, any of us suffering from seizures have that misfiring of neurons in common — a medical bond that we did not want or would ever choose. Though all epileptics have brains that betray them, a tonic-clonic epileptic brain betrays them to the point of cruelty.

Here's just one example: A woman in her seventies recently told me that her grandmother raised her cousin who had epilepsy. Though her grandmother was thoroughly ashamed of her cousin, this woman's grandmother often referred to her cousin in public, in an unashamedly audible voice, as a "freak." Casting her eyes downward, she added rather apologetically to me, "You know that was in a time when we did not know as much as we do today." Angry yet?

Along with the companionship of family and friends, I combat some of my isolation and anger through the internet "support groups." From my perspective, though I would rather have face-to-face interaction, it is encouraging to have someone write something as simple as, "I understand what you are going through." Though there is no faith affiliation associated with the group, members from all over the globe have prayed for me before surgery. They have also commented on my increasingly serendipitous meetings with fellow seizure sufferers in church. We have compared notes about hair loss to reinforce a caring and humor-filled group of support.

What I have discovered afresh is that no matter what kind of community is developed, sharing one's story and listening to others with epilepsy is curative. There is a connection in community. We are similar to one recovering alcoholic working with another recovering alcoholic, who are both trying to remain sober and sane so that we do not sink below the sorrow of our seizures.

Chapter Nineteen

Well, I'll Be

God is faithful; by him you were called into the fellowship of his son, Jesus Christ our Lord. I Corinthians 1:9

How lovely is your dwelling place, O Lord of hosts! My soul longs, indeed it faints for the courts of the Lord ... Psalm 84: 1-2a

Through the ages, Almighty God has moved his people to build houses of prayer and praise, and to set apart places for the ministry of his holy Word and Sacraments. BCP, p. 567

In the beginning of 2013, another community developed in a completely unexpected and astonishing way. I began to volunteer at St. Peter's Episcopal Church in Chattanooga, Tennessee. I stepped out of my comfort zone and went public about my epilepsy. No less than four members of the congregation came up to me and said that they still have seizures and that my outspoken, public sermons gave them some comfort and courage.

Here are some excerpts from those sermons:

Even with studying the text, it is a preaching commandment not to bring in those studies to the sermon in order to impress the listener. More than likely, it will produce even more yawns. If you will indulge me, I would like to bend the preaching rule and bring in three quotes concerning the little-known, most often-neglected bracketed portion of the Gospel text. One scholar wrote, "The **connection** *between the healing of the epileptic boy in relationship to the Transfiguration is not obvious and oddly placed." Another wrote, "There is no clear* **correlation** *between the healing of the epileptic in today's gospel text to the Transfiguration." Finally, I do not know whether to laugh or cry about one scholar's comment, "Yes, sometimes there is a* **connection** *between epilepsy and possession."*

Today's bracketed portion of Luke's Gospel tells of Jesus healing a young boy with epilepsy. Oh, before we go much further, I have not yet disclosed my reason for being on disability. Like the boy in today's Gospel text, I have epilepsy. (Pause) Imagine then how I, a person living with the disability of epilepsy, felt upon reading those scholars' comments: no connection to the Transfiguration; no correlation to the Gospel; (but a) connection of epilepsy to possession.

I have what is known as an "invisible disability." To look at me, most would never believe that I am living with a disability, much less epilepsy. Many kind and caring people have said to me, "George, you don't look disabled." I have the scars from neurosurgery to prove my disability. Only wisps of well-placed, thinning, "product-infused" hair can hide them. Others who have had neurosurgery are not so fortunate, but they are the courageous ones. They have a sort of sacramental "outward and visible" scar(s) that cannot be concealed. All I have as an outward and visible sign of epilepsy is this simple silver medical bracelet I wear on my left wrist. — Excerpts from sermon preached on February 10, 2013, at St. Peter's Episcopal Church.

The pain of being human is a complex concoction of physical, emotional, and spiritual turmoil. That mixture of damage is what happened to me. I was broken by just a one centimeter abnormal cluster of nerves in my brain called a Cavernous Malformation, and I began to have seizures. The physical, emotional and spiritual ache of this was too much for me. — Excerpt from sermon preached on March 10, 2013, at St. Peter's Episcopal Church.

Chapter Twenty

Emotions Above and Emotions Below

Trouble and anguish have come upon me, but your commandment is my delight. Psalm 119:143

Since, then, we have a great high priest who has passed through the heavens, Jesus, the Son of God, let us hold fast to our confession. Let us therefore approach the throne of grace with boldness, so that we may receive mercy and find grace to help in time of need. Hebrews 4:14,16

O Lamb of God, that takest away the sins of the world, have mercy upon us.
O Lamb of God, that takest away the sins of the world, have mercy upon us.
O Lamb of God, that takest away the sins of the world, grant us thy peace. BCP, p. 337

Fellow travelers who walk down the epilepsy road keep me from going out of my mind. There are times, however, that the psychosis strikes so unpredictably and swiftly it resembles venom being injected into the vein. Like a cobra rising up little by little and hissing, the madness becomes so serpent-like in intensity that fury and despair intermingle to take on what appears to be a personal presence. This phenomenon happened to me one evening in a very simple act that happens every morning and evening at 8:30. This is my seizure medication schedule. I am not proud of what happens next.

On one particular night, the Lamotrigine and Vimpat fell into the palm of my right hand. I sighed looking at one white and one orange pill. The sighing turned to a stinging stare as an actual hot and painful thin film of tears tore like saltwater at my eyeballs. And then a fury filled me full up. My temples began to beat as the "thump, thump, thump" reverberation reached a point that the drums of ridicule pounded and the cymbals of sarcasm clashed to their climax. With a rising, rasping voice that gushed forth uncontrollably, anguish and anger morphed into physical queasiness as my knees buckled and words tore out of my throat that are unfit to print.

The increase in volume was appalling and frightening to me. They were desperate utterances that were visceral, like burning bile. The adrenaline rush that followed made my eyes get even hotter, wetter and rawer. I was so sick of having to take pills to control my seizures. I was so sick of my life falling apart. I was so sick that my God had let me down. My collar had been shaken by seizures. My faith had been stirred, as well. I think my shaken collar and stirred faith is what I am trying to work out throughout this journal. You are a witness to how a real person who happens to have a vocation as a priest tries, fails, yet tries and tries again.

Since I am a priest, people have scrutinized me even closer to see how I have responded to my condition. For instance, there was a woman at a fundraiser where the proceeds were being raised for an Episcopal School down in Haiti. The story picks up here:

Part of the money for Haiti was being raised from a meal that cost two dollars to make and ten dollars to eat. Do the math. It is a well-deserved, eight-dollar profit going for an excellent ministry. I was seated at a table with two women; one was much more conversational than the other was. After the appropriate pleasantries were exchanged, the conversation gradually turned to the calamity of cancer. This was because the soundless friend of the woman at the table broke her silence and began to talk of her aggravation and depression concerning her reoccurring cancer. I went into a genuine caring priest and pastor mode and listened intently to her ache — physically, emotionally, and spiritually — associated with her diagnosis, treatment, and recovery. We had traveled in only a short matter of time from a surface level conversation to a deeper one as I shared my condition of epilepsy. I also shared that I am a priest.

At this point, something spiritually significant must have ignited and then detonated in the woman who was sitting at the same table. In one of those tones that instantly put me on my guard, the woman sat back, folded her arms and declared in a holier-than-thou voice, "You should be praising the Lord that you are still alive and getting healthy." With all the strength I could summon not to raise my voice, I muttered while fiercely glaring into her eyes, "Yes I should, but I am not there yet. I am still angry with God."

I often wonder what her reflection was on the event. What did she pass along to her friends? "I had dinner with this priest, and he actually said that he was mad at God. Can you believe it?" Your imagination of her facial expressions and vocal intonation can much more creatively fill in the rest of her conversation. Or did she even remember our conversation? Am I as judgmental of her as she of me? This anger is cancer-like and attacking my soul.

Chapter Twenty-One

PHASE III - BARGAINING

I Want What I Want When I Want It

Yet you, O Lord, are in the midst of us, and we are called by your name; do not forsake us! Jeremiah 14:9

My sheep hear my voice. I know them, and they follow me. John 10:27

Thy kingdom come, thy will be done ... BCP, p. 54

Bargaining is the phase that is defined exactly as it is written. "If I do this for you," my interior voice pleads, "then you will do this for me." In other words, I was making this deal with God. I am no different from others who make this similar quid pro quo deal with God. If you believe in God or a Higher Power, then this arrangement is simply ludicrous and not even logical. Think of it in these terms: a creature tells the Creator what to do and sets down the rules of how this arrangement is going to happen. This is the way I bargained, and I can only base this part of the journal on my experiences as a person of faith who believes in God.

The absurdity of telling God what to do falls under the rubric of the bargaining phase of grief. Bargaining with or without God is an illogical yet necessary step for anyone to move through the intricate sequence of grief. Bargaining is simply our direct, deepest desperation birthed into life. To skip this step of desperation is to diverge from the path of grief. To skip this step leads nowhere and stops grieving so that one is stuck in the goo of grief. In order to move forward, I had to be wrenchingly hopeless at this point in the epilepsy journey instead of unemotional and detached. You have to get honest with yourself and admit that you cannot regain your life on your own. This doubting priest turned to God in my desperation. As I have written before, go ahead and throw the first stone.

There is, nevertheless, some perceived sense to our emotion in this stage of grief. You think that only God can change the situation, and most, though not all would affirm this notion. The mistake we make in this stage of our grief is that we begin to define the tapered parameters of what it will take for God to change our situation.

We want parameters because we are so frantic. We want to regain some semblance of being in charge of our brains, so we have invited, more likely commanded, the Almighty to make our desperate longing come true. We want our will to be God's will. We want God on our own terms; we want God to fix our situation on our terms. Being a theologically trained person, I know that this is not how it works.

In my priestly presumption, I thought that God would hear my bargaining prayers and straight away stop my seizures. Oh, I also proceeded to justify my bargaining. Of course, my bargaining prayers of desperation would be in complete accord with what God needed to do because surely this is exactly what God wanted to do in the first place. God just needed me to remind God of exactly what needed to happen. Ironic? Ignorance? Arrogance? All three?

Did I think, as a priest, that God would be more likely to respond favorably to my bargaining? I am affronted even at my own pride. I even hate to reveal it in writing, but this is my life. It's raw and real, not perfect or polished in order to make it more palatable for the reader. My sarcasm makes me sick. I hope that my grief is eventually transformed into good grief for both of us.

Epilepsy is a loss. I am still grieving the loss of my health, my position, my predictability, my control. I cannot ever get those back. My bargaining turned to the deal of no longer having seizures in the present and future. I no longer could stand the thought of my brain betraying me ever again. My bargaining strategy summary — I will do anything, anything at all, if you will get rid of these seizures. I want my life back. The emphasis was on "my life back."

The following is a complex journal entry of a spiritual reflection that demonstrates in writing my desperation to place my situation back under some sort of control. It does fit in as a frantic endeavor to bring some spiritual significance as to where my life had taken me since numerous seizures and two neurosurgeries and how I wanted my life back:

There was absolutely nothing particularly ominous this day to indicate something peculiar was just about to happen. With my seizures now under control, I simply went running on one of my favorite routes. On this run, the turnaround point is at a cul-de-sac on Creekshire Drive. It is an attractive, albeit a tad bit humdrum, quiet, suburban street on Signal Mountain in Tennessee. The typical house is four to five thousand square feet with professionally landscaped, well-kept lawns that are sometimes separated by Tennessee scrub pine woods from other nice houses with professionally-landscaped and well-kept lawns.

To be straightforward, I like this run. It is both a paradox of civilized and untamed. Barking dogs with wagging tails are kept in their yards by electric fences. Just feet away from the canines, the occasional flock of wild turkeys will trot through or doe and fawn gracefully remain standing in the woods in semi-camouflage. It is as if turkey and deer are conscious of the absurdity of the circumstances. Even from this short distance, they can safely scoff at a dog taunting it to try and break the invisible, electric barrier and get shocked in the process.

As I continue to run, both the domesticated dog and untamed creatures of the forest simply stare at this two-legged oddity that moves with no particular purpose other than to exercise in a straight line and circle around at the end of the cul-de-sac where the pavement ends abruptly, and another part of the woods begins with a single step forward.

At this point in my run, a curious occurrence began to build in the silent shelter of the forest. Even though the end of the street was in sight, I did not see what was about to take place. With the illusion that all was ordinary, I trudged on under an indigo sky that in the swift snap of skin from thumb across middle finger promptly turned an uncanny, dark gray. A silent, sneaky vapor pushed into the gray. As if caught in a wet tunnel of claustrophobic haze, I was abruptly enveloped in a moist mist of fog. One moment, all was well; the next, the fog rolled in. I could not have escaped the fog no matter how fast, or in which direction, I ran.

This event actually did transpire. Though fog is commonplace on Signal Mountain, I have never experienced it like I did on that day. This fog, if it is possible, had something about it that went beyond a natural phenomenon. It wrapped me up and took me over — possessed me if you will. It took on an asphyxiating existence. It was personal as if the fog forged its way into my brain and seized me.

"Before the fog rolled in" my life was moving right along as well as one can plan such things to go. Marriage, children, and career were moving right along, like the Dow Jones in a profitable market. There were, of course, the inevitable lows that life brings, but the highs far outnumbered them. For instance, my wife and I were just about to celebrate twenty-four years of marriage. Each and every year together, Anne and I were growing closer and closer as we celebrated our lives together.

Our four children were doing well in school. By this time in 2009, our oldest child, Neil was in college. Our second born, Drew was winning award after award for his artwork. Kelly was discovering a new gift and talent in her writing. Preston was beginning to bud as an actor. They were all A and B students. The grade of a C was rare. Churches were inviting and courting me into their search processes. Vocationally, I was climbing the ladder of clergy success — I shudder and am ashamed even to utilize that vocabulary and put it down in writing. Marriage, children, and career were all going along as planned. But that all was about to change. Plans are an illusion. Control is an impostor. I have always said and preached this, but did I believe it? This was about to be tested.

In the midst of my life of stunning blue sky, I was engulfed by something I did not perceive coming. Abruptly from out of the blue sky, three centimeters of the color red — blood — blasted out in all directions from a Cavernous Malformation that had hemorrhaged. A spot of only one centimeter deep within my left frontal lobe bled and altered the rest of my brain and body. My mapped-out life then transformed around me and also those around me exponentially. No one signed up for this, but it enveloped everyone. Everything radically changed in my well-kept life when I was betrayed, betrayed by my brain.

Chapter Twenty-Two

The Bargaining Boom and Bust

If this plan or this undertaking is of human origin, it will fail... Acts 5:38

For sure I know the plans I have for you, says the Lord ... Jeremiah 29:11a

Do you promise to follow and obey him as your Lord? I do. BCP, p. 303

While reading the list that follows, you may consider my bargaining to be nothing more than healthy things to do in order to be a better person. Certainly, they are ways of being healthy and being a better person, but they also reveal my extreme anxiety because they always came with the line, "I will do this if you will do that." Again, I was making deals with God. I was bargaining in a conditional way. The caveat was always, "I will do this if you will do that."

"I'll give up candy and eat healthier food if you will take away my seizures."

When I began to drool at the frozen Milky Way candy bar hidden away in the back of the freezer, I promptly began to have second thoughts about this deal. If it meant not having seizures, I would give up old habits. With such a sacrifice on my part, God would be obliged to exonerate me from seizures. I think you will smirk at this, as well as the following bargains I was striking with God.

"I will not react negatively to stressful situations if you will take away my seizures."

This is the most insane deal I could ever have made. For instance, all of my exercise by running hardly ever alleviated my anxiety. I, still, was dogged by stress and could not stop that vicious hound from tracking me down. I could not outdistance the psychological strain snapping at my heels. My doctor eventually put me on Atenolol to decrease my blood pressure and mellow me out. This was another crushing defeat. I would never be able to fulfill my end of the bargain with God using my own wits and wherewithal.

My mother recounts that this off-putting attribute in me started very early on. She reminisced to me of a fishing story when I was about six. I was having no luck catching but looked longingly at bountiful schools of bream just below the surface. I kept casting out worm after worm. When you catch nothing, there are standby fishing phrases that go, "all I was doing was drowning worms" and "that's why they call it 'fishing' and not 'catching'" that are supposed to defuse the pain with humor. Well, not with a six-year-old. It was simple. I just was not that complicated. I had reached my limit and forcefully threw down my Zebco 202 and ran flat out into the water wildly snatching at the bream that had scattered straight away. All I caught was humiliation.

Anne, as well as our children, could give you copious examples of how stress affects me negatively. It can all be summed up in something one of our children coldly said to me — "Dad, you must be the most impatient person I have ever met!"

"I will continue to exercise but not in the extreme way I used to do if you will take away my seizures."

Some of the time, I exercised to extremes. The lengthy, steep inclines of Signal Mountain and the challenging, rocky trails of Prentice Cooper State Park were extreme exercise opportunities that were hard to pass up to an adrenaline junkie. Both were so temptingly close by. For example, the hills were literally outside my front door, and Prentice Cooper was barely a mile away from my house. I honestly did fulfill my end of the bargain due to two issues: 1) most of my seizures came during hard runs and 2) surgery prevented me from exercising excessively hard. Literally, I did stop exercising to extremes. The truth, nevertheless, is that I kept my end of the bargain by finding the loopholes. It was not an honest way of keeping my end of the bargain. How could God be so cruel as not to honor the bargain that I had so clearly and cleverly set up? Desperation makes desperate people make desperate and dumb deals.

"I will be a better husband, father, priest, control my temper, not ever cuss, be a better person if you will take away my seizures."

What the heck? Why not go "whole hog" and become the most incredible person you've ever met? God would most certainly take away my seizures after I became such a Saint. Unfortunately, the title and name of St. George was already taken. Good thing, too.

"I will do almost anything if you will take away my seizures."

I had lost complete touch with reality. My neurologist professionally confronted me with the statement, "Mr. Choyce, you are talking about a significant diet change to last for a lifetime." He then prodded, "Are you willing to take that on?" It is utterly uncomfortable to put it down in black and white in the pages of this journal for you to see. I hope the good offsets the bad by being this brutally candid about the absurdity that my life had become.

While this ambitious list is filled with fine things to do, the items on the list cannot continually be completed by a person. Most of the contents on the list cannot even be accomplished for a brief amount of time. It is futility to try fulfilling them even over a lifetime. Some of them can be carried out, perhaps for a time. Did I think that I could attain them because I had more "willpower" than the average person? Maintaining these transformative ways of living puts more strain on you. Ironic, isn't it? This pressure to be seizure-free is a trigger — you guessed it — for further seizures.

Chapter Twenty-Three

The Tragic Transition to Depression

Beloved, do not be surprised at the fiery ordeal that is taking place among you to test you, as though something strange were happening to you. I Peter 4: 12

Out of the depths I cry to you, O Lord.
Lord, hear my voice!
Let your ears be attentive
to the voice of my supplications! Psalm 130:1-2

We do earnestly repent,
and are heartily sorry for these our misdoings;
the remembrance of them is grievous unto us,
the burden of them is intolerable. BCP p. 331

O nce again, this is the dreadful emotional, spiritual, and physical power of seizures. You will do anything to get rid of the seizures. When you reach this point, something begins to occur in the grief journey. Your trip is about to transform. You get to a point on the path where you did not want to go. It finally sank in for me that even Almighty God was not going to deliver me from seizures in the exact manner I had prescribed. Completely lost and maddened in my grief, I concluded that God had broken the promise of "take away my seizures" in our bargain.

Here in the journey, the cinder of depression develops and wraps you up in a crushing cloak of claustrophobic despair. Your world is crumbling around you. You cannot escape the cage of epilepsy. The walls of depression are too dark and deep to scale.

I could not heave myself out of the pit and escape the head organ that had betrayed me. Once the depression was settling in, the bargaining became a trickle. In this transition time, a combination of fact and emotion regarding the brain began to fuse in my thinking. The catalyst for this step was a conversation I referred to earlier when a pharmacist friend of mine said, "The brain is basically a universe that is largely unexplored." I did know, nevertheless, some elementary facts. For instance, the brain is the largest of all human organs. It is the center of the nervous system and controls all your bodily functions. Unlike a leg or arm, your brain cannot be amputated to save gangrene from spreading to save the body. Amputate the brain, and you die.

On an emotional level regarding the brain, I also "knew" some things from my disconcerting experience. My understanding was that the gangrene of misfiring neurons in the brain spreads like toxin first to itself and then outward into your body. You seize. Your brain betrays you. It gets personal.

The brain seems more than physical some of the time. To me, my betraying brain is more than physical, and it took on a personal presence of malevolence. Though it is the birthplace of my seizures, it is as if the bubbling chaos of primeval ruthlessness resides there. Epilepsy enveloped me in a cackling cloud of darkness from the inside out. You can almost hear a malicious, maniacal screech between your ears. Since this is my journal, I should also add that I do not hear audible voices or even voices in my head. These "voices" were more shadowy thoughts.

Some people have pushed the perceived personal evil of epilepsy to the breaking point, however. They have construed certain Biblical texts to support that seizures equal satanic influence. For instance, when chapter nine of the Gospel of Luke is interpreted literally, there is a dangerous conclusion that seizures are a sign of demonic possession. Here is a portion of that text:

On the next day, when they had come down from the mountain, a great crowd met him. Just then a man from the crowd shouted, 'Teacher, I beg you to look at my son; he is my only child. Suddenly a spirit seizes him, and all at once he shrieks. It throws him into convulsions until he foams at the mouth; it mauls him and will scarcely leave him. I begged your disciples to cast it out, but they could not.' Jesus answered, 'You faithless and perverse generation, how much longer must I be with you and bear with you? Bring your son here.' While he was coming, the demon dashed him to the ground in convulsions. But Jesus rebuked the unclean spirit, healed the boy, and gave him back to his father. And all were astounded at the greatness of God. Luke 9:37-45 NRSV

Ironically, perhaps providentially, even comically, my first sermon on February 10, 2013, after a year and three month hiatus from the pulpit contained the previous Lukan text.

I do not believe that epilepsy is an irrefutable sign of demonic possession, but there are certain Christians who irrefutably believe it. It is understandable how some onlookers to a tonic-clonic seizure would think that something malevolent was going on as the person writhes on the ground and foams at the mouth. Some well-meaning Christians have gone so far as to perform an exorcism on the person suffering from epilepsy believing that a demon must be expelled in order for the person to no longer have a seizure.

At this point in my journey through grief, epilepsy again morphed into something more than physical. It became a personal presence of gloom, which is a much more subtle and successful demon in and of itself. My bargaining with God could not stop this emotional and spiritual experience of seizures any more than it stopped the physical seizures themselves. I wish that I had this part of the grief journey under control. I failed miserably or perhaps I succeeded exceedingly because in going through this experience it led me to the next necessary step of grief.

The bargaining with God did not stop my last documented seizure. It happened, in all places, at Church.

Chapter Twenty-Four

PHASE IV - DEPRESSION

Diverse Depression

To this day I have had help from God, and so I stand here ...
Acts 26:22

In my distress I cry to the Lord, that he may answer me:
Deliver me, O Lord ... Psalm 120:1-2a

I lay my hands upon you in the Name of our Lord and Savior
Jesus Christ, beseeching him to uphold you and fill you with
his grace, that you may know the healing power of his love.
Amen. BCP, p. 456

S ome of the following scenarios are chronologically out of place, yet they are all illustrations of how depression subtly invades all of the stages of grief. The depression stage of grief was not permanent — at least for me it was not. The acceptance phase that I am in now and probably will be in for the rest of my life did finally come from the diving board of depression.

Depression goes back and forth in its invasion of grief. It can, nevertheless, lead to acceptance when it comes to healthy grieving.

I had tried everything. Neither Cyberknife surgery nor anticonvulsant medication brought about a cessation to the seizures. Helplessness and hopelessness sank into my spirit — not really a stirred faith but more of a stagnant one. The sensation of depression actually felt like a weight. Even others said things like,

I can see it in your face, and it's not just your meds.

You're not yourself.

You're not confident like you once were.

And they were right.

By this point in my epilepsy journey, I had stopped moving. I did not want to move at all. All of the fighting had stuck me to the insect paper of seizures. The more I moved, the more my hands and legs still succumbed to seizures. I was worn out. Things were coming undone all around me, and I could not tie them up in a nice, neat package of repair. The medicine and Cyberknife surgery had not fixed me. I was falling apart. To top all of this off, one of the seizure medications that is supposed to be a "mood- alterer" could not alter my mood to get me out of the murky funk of depression.

It was awful. First, my brain had an area in it that was causing the seizures. Secondly, somewhere in my brain, chemical signals were being sent that pushed me over into the quicksand of sinking sadness. This was a double betrayal by my brain. A scorner was in those misfiring neurons irreverently smiling at me with a scathing question, "And just what are you going to do about it?" Adding to the inquiry, the ridiculing betrayal of my left frontal lobe inserted the insult, "I can do whatever I please. There is nothing, absolutely nothing, you can do about it. I've gotten to you. I'm inside your head now." Again, this voice was not audible, but still it spoke to me.

For me, it was "game on." The gauntlet was thrown down. My brain had slapped me in the face. I needed help. This is where my competitive nature was an advantage.

I had a choice to make. I could either go the stride with seizures unaccompanied or have others join me. My epilepsy journey could not be taken solo, or I would be mired in depression. Though medication can help, the human touch is greater than chemicals. It is others, who choose to walk with you, who will not let you sink in a bog of hopelessness.

This image of a bog came to me while watching "The Hound of the Baskervilles" from the Sherlock Holmes collection. In this setting, the moors of the West Country of England, there are treacherous spots where a novice passerby can step in the wrong place and be suddenly sucked under in a bog. To make the situation doubly dangerous, it is sometimes impossible to see the Grimpen Mire due to the white fog that obscures them. You either avoid the area altogether — which I could not do since it was my brain that had "mired" me — or you could be saved by someone who is not in the bog but holds out something for the victim to grab hold of, like a branch.

People began to hold out a long branch for me to grab, but it was up to me to reach out and not be too proud to grab it. Family and friends are not going to go into the bog with you. If they did sink under, they could not help you. By staying safely out of the bog, they can help to pull you out.

Anne and I have stubborn friends who will not let us go through my struggle with seizures alone. They frequently bring us food, invite us out, visit, call, work on the house, and even help us out financially to pay off medical bills, as they are able. In essence, while I am stuck in the bog, they hold out whatever branches they can offer. They actually say things like this:

Thank you for the privilege of allowing me to help you and your family.

It makes me feel good that I am making a difference.

Let us know if there is any more we can do.

The professionals have also joined in the fray against the loneliness and the despair of dwindling finances. For instance, my neurologist always provides a free month's supply of one of my anti-seizure medications out of the office stock of samples. The Office Manager has told the Manufacturer's Representative of our plight, and he routinely brings in additional samples to meet my monthly anti-seizure medication needs. The Office Manager passes along to me that he, in her words, "always leaves with a smile." Here is the brutal reality of epilepsy medication — I priced a month's supply at my local pharmacy for just this one medication, and the total was $574! You do the math for a year.

In addition to the vast reduction of prescription medication cost, our car repair shop gave us a discount on their labor. That was all about to change. Here is an example: There is appallingly little this particular shop can do on the price of parts; they would if they could. Very recently, nonetheless, I asked the owner — before the repair began — if he could do the labor portion of a particular repair job for $75. His direct quote, in a rural Tennessean back-of-Signal Mountain accent, was, "I caan but I won'ts. Aw, come on, man. I already gives you a break. I knows what's goin' on, but I gotta make a living."

Another professional mechanic, who, like me, is on disability, refuses to charge us for any of his skilled labor. When we have little left in the bank account until the next disability check comes in, and we also need a car repair, he does the repair for nothing. (He would never forgive me if I put his name in print.) When I have pulled out a twenty dollar bill from my wallet to offer him something, he simply ignores it. If I am persistent at all, he snaps, "Put that away!" He shakes his head, scowls, but then he grins.

Some months, however, it has come down to an assessment of buying food or paying off medical bills and/or utility bills. What a dreadful dilemma for a mom and dad. What would you do? For example, one particular month's remaining resources were so abysmal that there was no money left for either food or bills. For Anne and me, the resolution, though painful, was plain.

Here is what happened: On one day, I stood in the food pantry of the church where I volunteer. I did not want for anyone to discern that I was there but felt like I had a moral obligation to tell someone something regarding my presence. My feet felt bolted to the concrete floor. I was numb. I stared at boxes and cans. Looking at the food, a wave of queasiness swept over me. It had come to the point that I was not only looking at food; I was looking at the starchy-types of food — rice, dried beans, and potato flakes — to inspect what would be the most filling to get us through the month. On one hand, I was crushed. On the other, a portion of the Magnificat from St. Luke's Gospel resounded over and over and over in my head:

He has filled the hungry with good things ...

He has filled the hungry with good things ...

He has filled the hungry with good things ...

It had come to this. I used to be the rector of a large church where the pay was secure and the weekly groceries for my family could be taken for granted. When indigents came to that church, they were directed to food pantries on Signal Mountain or in Chattanooga. I was now standing in one of those food pantries where I had directed indigents. Three centimeters in my brain had brought me to my knees in some mishmash of humility and disgrace in front of canned food and boxed potato flakes.

At this point in my factual story, an employee of the church walked into the pantry because the light was on. My head turned slowly to the left. No words were exchanged. There was a pause, but it was not awkward. There was no humiliation. There was just grace. There was quiet. And there was food — food. She gathered small, strong cardboard boxes and quietly helped me load them. My dignity was spared.

Moreover, clergy colleagues began to hear about the Choyces' predicament through an email — an international technical branch, per se — that a seminary classmate of mine sent out to the VTS class of '92. Connections have been gradually reestablished due to my epilepsy.

Chapter Twenty-Five

Depression Detours

I will put my trust in him ... Hebrews 2:13

For he will command his angels concerning you
to guard you in all your ways.
On their hands they will bear you up... Psalm 91:11-12a

Heavenly Father, giver of life and health: Comfort and relieve
your sick servant George, and give your power of healing to
those who minister to his needs, that he may be strengthened
in his weakness and have confidence in your loving care;
through Jesus Christ our Lord. Amen. BCP, p. 459

Another such branch that was held out to me was by a radiologist friend of ours. His medical knowledge was his incalculable gift to Anne and me. As I referenced earlier, he came over to the house and sat down with us in the kitchen for a total of one hour and twenty minutes. In a frank yet friendly medical manner, he laid out all of the options. I wrote the following choices down on a piece of paper:

1) Do nothing.
2) Increase the dosage of my current anticonvulsants.
3) Switch to a different combination of anticonvulsants.
4) Have surgery to remove the source of the seizures.

The verdict had finally come to Anne and me with some clarity. The surgery was our best hope for the seizures to diminish or vanish completely. With all of the outpouring of love and support from family and friends, I had neurosurgery to eradicate the miniscule area where an EEG had determined the severe seizures were emanating. All of the scar tissue from the previous surgery and the vestiges of the blood from the hemorrhage were going to be excised from deep within my left frontal lobe. It was time for me to be pulled out of the bog. It was on November 28, 2011, that I had the surgery.

On that morning, Anne drove me to the hospital. She let me talk when I needed to talk, let me remain silent by not breaking the silence with idle talk and reassured me that we were not going to be late. I always worry about being on time.

Anne just gets me. She knows me. She knows when I need conversation and when I need silence. The morning of November 28, 2011, was no different, which is astounding considering the fact that I was scheduled for neurosurgery just three hours after we left the house.

Getting into the Operating Room is like running a gauntlet, which in this surgical context is a good thing. Over and over, I was posed the questions, "What is your name?" and "What are you having done today?" Some form of "George Choyce" and "removal of a Cavernous

Malformation" were my rote responses. I was so tempted to, as the British say, get "cheeky " and say "George Choyce; hysterectomy."

I refrained from bad humor just prior to a paper, blue and white-striped surgical bracelet being affixed around my wrist, since this was the medical team that would have my brain in their hands. Anne then helped me into one of those tie-in-the-back hospital gowns. We said, "I love you," at least five times followed by at least five kisses. A stretcher was brought in, and there was one more, "I love you," followed this time by two kisses.

Riding on the stretcher was a peculiar experience. I was lying on my back and experienced four sensations: the pleasant friction of the wheels of the stretcher rolling along; the gentle thumps where the floor and elevator met; the burning of the institutional hospital types of lights hypnotically spaced uniformly hanging over my head; the backward and forward, side to side pulling and pushing by the orderly. I was completely out of control, which served me well since I would be under someone else's control as my scalp, skull, and brain were going to be in my medical teams' control in the next hour. Even before the operation, something new was happening. The brain that betrayed me was submitting itself to the consideration that this operation was one step closer to the eradication of my seizures. Perhaps even my brain was succumbing to the hope it would stop misfiring and that the clerical collar would stop shaking.

I ultimately made it into the pre-op area, where once again I was asked my identity and the purpose of my operation. At this point, the anesthesiologists closed in around me from both sides of the stretcher. You could actually see their nose hairs from my angle, along with the pores of their skin.

They got down to business. That is one way of putting it. Multicolored hollow lines with differing widths were then inserted into my arms. Some were very skinny and snaked their way into my veins; the others were wider and clear. It did not hurt but watching these skinny lines go into your arms is something best suited for a cheesy horror film. This single medical procedure signified to me that there was no going back at this point. I was hooked up and ready to go.

At this moment, I do remember one of the anesthesiologists saying, "We're now going to give you some medicine to relax you." The sensation began, and it was like looking at the lines of a highway ripple by when you are in a car, except these lines were observed on the ceiling. For some reason, I was blinking rather rapidly. One other thing I remembered is that a colleague of mine came in and prayed for me. I looked up at him and said in an exceptionally sincere, yet exceedingly slurred and anesthetic-induced speech, "Bob, I just wanted to say that you're ..." Nothing else came out. Down the hall I went as I completely lost consciousness.

The surgery was performed, and then I was wheeled into the recovery room. It was just that matter-of-fact. You go into surgery with a Cavernous Malformation; you come out Cavernous Malformationless.

I remembered nothing else until I woke up in the recovery room with Anne standing at the foot of the bed. We kissed again. The healing was beginning.

Chapter Twenty-Six

The Force of the Family

And this is my prayer, that your love may overflow more and more ... Philippians 1:9

As the Father has loved me, so have I loved you; abide in my love. John 15:9

Turn the hearts of the parents to the children, and the hearts of children to the parents ... BCP, p. 829

I think one of the most complex facets of having epilepsy is how my seizures unintentionally involve others, especially those in my family. I was willing to go to any length to be rid of these seizures by having brain surgery, but it was not just my operation. Although the operation was sterile, and the ICU room was sterile, emotions are not sterile. Anne and two of our children, along with my parents came to visit me during ICU visiting hours. I was in a pitiable position.

The frontal lobe area of my head was covered in gauze and surgical tape. By the way, when I retched or sneezed an audible "whoosh, whoosh" sound emanated from the top of my head. Just thought you ought to know that anecdote as an aside of what brain surgery can do. I had never sensed or heard anything like this. I finally figured out that this reverberation was the literal sound of my skull reforming.

To get back to my situation — my arms still had those lines in succession throughout my veins. There was a modest amount of dried blood on my arms and neck. I do not remember much of the visit other than it was apparent that Kelly was visibly upset; she cried. Preston kept it all inside, but his silence along with a pasty, green-tinged face told the same story. I can only speak for myself; my seizures had pulled in my family not only when they were occurring but when I was doing what I considered was paramount to control those seizures. I hate epilepsy!

My family has also transported laughter onto the path of epilepsy. When it all gets too serious, my family provides incredible, irreverent humor. In my experience, humor has helped me in this epilepsy journey. Their best snappy comeback is when I am tumbling over my words and stumbling over my feet. There is a tap on my shoulder, followed by, "It's okay, Dad, we all know you're on drugs." Of course, this is true to a certain extent due to my seizure medications. I immediately found this funny, but it also hurt my head when I laughed.

Recently, my youngest children have forcefully tapped their temples with two fingers while sticking out their front teeth and making a clicking noise. Sometimes they embellish my medication side effects and say rather sheepishly, "Dad, I told my teacher and my school counselor that you're on drugs." There is then a long pause for dramatic effect when their whole facial countenance transforms, followed by a loud snort, "Just kidding!"

Just recently, my daughter asked me to describe the operation to her. I showed her pictures of the brain from the internet. Chiefly, we went into detail about the lobes of the brain. I pointed to the place on my scalp where my scar was and asked her what part of the brain it was. She proudly stated, "The left frontal lobe." "Correct," I enthusiastically interjected. "So," she continued, "it's like your brain is a deep dish pizza, and they went in and took out a piece of pepperoni." I guess that's one way of putting it. Since Kelly is an especially talented writer, she confidently went on and proclaimed, "My next paper will be entitled 'They Took a Piece of Pepperoni out of my Dad's Brain.'"

Some of these moments of hilarity come in the least expected times. For instance, my oldest son was traveling to Australia for a Work Study experience for the last semester of his Junior Year in college. There is a somewhat famous comedy movie that takes place in Australia, so we watched it on one of the last nights we were all together.

In one scene, a male character tries to describe a beautiful woman he has just met to his best friend. The first character uses no recognizable words; instead, he begins this over-the-top form of nonverbal body language. He shakes and jerks in front of his best friend who clearly does not have any clue as to what he is trying to get across. Finally, his best friend in utter frustration blurts out, "She's epileptic?" We all laughed, and this time my head did not hurt at all. I do, nevertheless, accept and respect the reality that there are plenty of people with epilepsy and their caregivers who do not find such humor to be the least bit amusing.

Most of the time, epilepsy in the movies or in other popular media continues to reinforce a stigma that those with epilepsy have mental illness, low intelligence or even demonic possession. In my situation, my family, however, was comfortable enough with me and my seizures that they could laugh. And they had earned that right ... at least with me. The depression was beginning to lift.

Chapter Twenty-Seven

Depression Detours,
Part II

Today the Lord has obtained your agreement: to be his treasured people, as he promised people ... Deuteronomy 26:18

I will take you as my people, and I will be your God. Exodus 6:7

O God, who created all peoples in your image, we thank you for the wonderful diversity of races and cultures in the world. Enrich our lives by ever-widening circles of fellowship, and show us your presence in those who differ most from us, until our knowledge of your love is made perfect in our love for all your children; through Jesus Christ our Lord. Amen. BCP, p. 840

At this part of my journey through grief, I took a fascinating detour and began to ask diverse questions along the way.

Are there famous living people who have revealed they have seizures? There is a dilemma to those of us who have seizures. Do we hide them or do we come out publicly and divulge our condition? Some of us have no choice. Our seizures happen publicly. I could not hide my seizures, especially when they occurred in front of the congregation or the midst of a parish activity. Another public seizure led to my resignation. Gossip stretched my medical condition from the heights of mountains into the surrounding valley area below including Chattanooga, Tennessee. Some might call it courage that I acknowledged my epilepsy and perhaps it is. I really had no choice.

I sense some of the most courageous people out there are the public figures who do not mask the fact that they have seizures. They stand to lose so much with either that Scarlet E of Epilepsy or Scarlet S of Seizures hanging around their necks for all to see. Think of what would happen if they had a seizure while on live television or during a "take" for a movie. My story with epilepsy is a part of a much larger context; even prosperous and prominent people are not exempt from the same neurological condition that touches all types of people.

The courageous also includes the common woman, man, and child who have epilepsy. Though we are not public figures, most of us who are suffering from seizures have what I and others would call a "hidden disability." We just do not look the part. There is no wheelchair or cane for most of us, though the wheelchair and cane are a daily part of the lives of others who suffer from seizures.

Again, I just do not look the part of someone with epilepsy. Even in my neighborhood, my neighbors see me out walking the dogs or running or gardening. They ask how I am doing because they know I am recovering from brain surgery. I respond that I am still recovering from surgery and still on disability. As I referred to earlier, without fail they respond, "Well, you look good. You don't look disabled to me."

I am the face of epilepsy for the people around me. You have met people with epilepsy; you just did not know it at the time unless they said something. We epileptics (this word is currently discouraged) do not look like what you were anticipating. We don't look like we are living with a disability. For the most part, we come across just like everyone else.

Once people ascertain that I have seizures, some of those conversations end up going like this: "Uh, I know this guy whose mother has a friend whose cousin has epilepsy. Uh, I really don't know much about it or where he lives or anything else, but I do know he has epilepsy." This is where there is an awkward silence in the dialogue. I usually try to do a bit more engagement and education within the context of the conversation, but it often ends with a hasty and uncomfortable, "Well, I've got to go. Have a nice day."

I really do get it. It's uncomfortable because they may think that I am going to have a seizure right there in front of them. Okay, I really do get that epilepsy is an uncomfortable subject. I do get that seizures are scary. I do not get why you might be anxious of me. I am a person. I am not contagious.

One friend and colleague put it succinctly and simply by saying, "Just tell us what to do." He pressed on, "If you have a seizure in the pulpit, what do we do? If you have a seizure at the altar, what do we do? Tell us what to do, and we'll do it."

Another friend and colleague of mine put it this way to combat all the prejudice he knew that I had been subjected to: "If you have a seizure, we'll deal with it. If you wet yourself, we'll dry you off. If you defecate on yourself, we'll clean you up. We just want you to come out and be with us." All of these comments of support mean more to me than these words in black and white can ever convey.

Let's try this: Perhaps the two of us can partner even more profoundly in this epilepsy journey. Perhaps this is why I wrote this journal, and perhaps this is why you are reading it — to make a simple or profound transformation in a single life or in countless lives. You and I may be just ordinary people, who together make extraordinary things happen. You could be a famous and influential person, who could use your fame and funds to make a dynamic difference in the lives of those suffering from seizures. We need a face. We need a name. Is God calling? You? Me? Us?

Michael J. Fox is the recognized face for Parkinson's disease. And proud of it. Not that I wish epilepsy on anyone, but epilepsy needs a Michael J. Fox. He's got credibility and integrity when it comes to Parkinson's because he is a person living with it. In other words, he lives gracefully with a disability. I could list some of the famous actors and musicians who are rumored to have epilepsy. There are, nevertheless, athletes you will read about very soon who announce and affirm that they have epilepsy. Almost all actors and musicians would deny that they still have seizures but insist that they grew out of them. Yes, "grew out of them" is the verbatim expression people use so as not to ruin their career.

There are, even so, living sports figures that have seizures. They choose not to hide their medical condition from the public. Some athletes who live with epilepsy have audaciously announced to coaches, players, and fans — at a potential cost to their career — "I have seizures," or "I live with epilepsy." I will show my bias about public figures with epilepsy and begin with football players.

I am a Pittsburgh Steelers fan, and that is putting it mildly. I even go as far as to correctly pronounce the name of my favorite football team — the "Stihlers." Additionally, my Myron Cope terrible towel hangs visibly in my bedroom all year long and not just during football season. It is draped in the corner of the widescreen television like a sacred altar linen blessing the field of play during the fall of football season. The yellow of the terrible towel is now beginning to fade. The towel itself is becoming threadbare from the use and abuse it has received being waved over my head. Anne and our children have given me Steelers mugs, flags, blankets, and even a doll or two for Christmas and birthday presents.

I was elated when I discovered that former Pittsburgh Steelers' guard and six-time Pro Bowler, Alan Faneca, does not conceal his epilepsy from the public. He has the power of a professional football player and the weakness of someone living with epilepsy, someone like me. Faneca volunteers with the Epilepsy Foundation and works with others who live with seizures. In other words, he is as authentic to epilepsy as Michael J. Fox is to Parkinson's disease.

Other football players with epilepsy include Samari Rolle and Jason Snelling. Rolle played Cornerback for the Tennessee Oilers, who later became the Tennessee Titans. Even though I currently live in Tennessee, I just could not bring myself to be a Titans' fan. This does not, however, diminish my respect for Samari Rolle, who ended his football career as a Baltimore Raven before retiring due to a neck injury. He went public on November 17, 2007, with what had been previously referred to as an "undisclosed illness." Rolle disclosed that his illness was epilepsy. Additionally, Atlanta Falcons Running Back, Jason Snelling has epilepsy and has been public about his seizures since being drafted by the Falcons.

These three professional football players have come out publicly to disclose that they have seizures but take all the medical precautions necessary to play professional football. By revealing their seizures to their coaches, these athletes took the risk of not playing professional football at all because of the danger of having a seizure during a game and costing their team a win. To put it mildly, I think highly of these athletes, their teammates and the coaches associated with their respective teams. By revealing their seizures to their teams and the public, they chanced sacrificing their careers because they were not "normal." What amazing role models!

As far as I can tell, Faneca, Rolle, and Snelling have received nothing but support from their teams. I wonder why then do some with epilepsy find it so hard to gain support in their places of work? Or do they (we) just hide it well? Are athletes with epilepsy treated better than the rest of us? What am I missing here?

Chapter Twenty-Eight

From Coaches to Christians to the Classics

Let us now sing the praises of famous men and women, our ancestors in their generations. Ecclesiasticus 44:1

I know my own and my own know me ... John 10:14b

Grant, O God, that your holy and life-giving Spirit may so move every human heart, that barriers which divide us may crumble, suspicions disappear, and hatreds cease; that our divisions being healed, we may live in justice and peace; through Jesus Christ our Lord. Amen. BCP, p. 823

B elow is an article written by me that was published in September 2013 about another sports figure. I had never even heard of him before his public seizure. There have been many parts of my journal that I am not proud of, but I am of this one. It shows how far I have come in the four years since my first seizure.

You could not have scripted this one any better. Both the name and the event were made for a movie, but this all happened in real life. The name is Coach Kill. What a name for a football head coach! I also like the alliteration of putting an exaggerated emphasis on the hard "C" and the "K". The event was a public tonic clonic seizure on the sideline just seconds from halftime witnessed by thousands in the stands and even more on television. When you put it all together, Coach Kill of the University of Minnesota's Golden Gophers had a seizure in public while coaching a football game against the Western Illinois University Leathernecks on September 15th, 2013.

Suddenly, every sportscast — and I flipped through numerous channels to verify what I am writing — carried some mention, either verbally or scrolling across the bottom of the screen, referencing Coach Kill's seizure. Now I don't know about you, but my experience of the news that Coach Kill has epilepsy was, to my total surprise, one of strong emotions. First, let me write something in the hope that something positive comes out of Coach Kill's seizure. In my opinion, hearing or reading the words "seizure" and "epilepsy" on cable television is a good thing. Like I have written previously, it brings our condition out of the dark and into the light of the public's collective conscious. Second of all, I just felt bad for Coach Kill. It was not a patronizing pity of "poor thing." It was something deeply moving in the way of an emotional connection to the previously-unknown Coach Kill, since I have had numerous seizures in public. Have you ever felt a similar connection to someone else who has suffered one or more public seizures, or any seizure for that matter?

From this unexpected bond with Coach Kill, I began to examine his life. His story is quite inspiring. He really is just another person who is trying to get his seizures under control so that he can do his job, as well as be able to drive again. Sound familiar? Now his job is probably different from most jobs. He is the Head Football Coach of the University of Minnesota. He makes 2.1 million dollars a year. It is still a job, his job. He also wants to get back to driving his pickup truck with the window down while listening to country music. Our details differ from his; however, most of us work closely with our neurologist or neurosurgeon to bring our seizures under control so that we can get on with our lives of going to school, work, volunteering, as well as driving. I would add to do these things without the fear of cruel ridicule. Again, sound familiar?

Coach Kill is not immune to this immature and pathetic phenomenon of ridicule. If anything, he is probably more susceptible to it since he is a public figure. It is not surprising then that when I kept on researching the man with whom I had suddenly bonded, I found that my hunch was right. For example, ESPN columnist Rick Reilly wrote an article entitled "Just killing it. Golden Gophers Coach turned his public seizure into a teaching moment." Reilly writes,

> *Kill never even used to utter the word "epilepsy" until he got hate emails after a seizure in the postgame after the Northwestern game last season. One writer called him a "freak." One tweet encouraged Minnesota to "fire the flopper."*

And this is 2013. Can you believe it? Yes, of course you can. How's your blood pressure now?

Coach Kill probably wishes that his movie would end with his walking out of the theater of seizures, getting into his pickup truck and riding down a road called Normal, while listening to country music. But that is not going to happen, at least for now. In the meantime, the coach will take his licks

— the cheap shots — from anonymous naysayers and turn the negatives into teachable moments and as inspiration to keep talking about epilepsy. We can do the same. While not many of us are in the same spotlight that Coach Kill is in, we have the bond of seizures. It is our reality. Together we make a great cast. What part are you going to play in the movie?

Along with contemporary public figures like Coach Kill, there are famous deceased persons who had epilepsy. They too must have taken their fair share of "cheap shots", or did they hide their epilepsy from the public? According to coping-with-epilepsy.com, here is a partial list of famous persons known to have had Epilepsy: Alexander the Great, Aristotle, Alfred the Great, Alfred Lord Tennyson, Vincent van Gogh, Charles Dickens, Alfred Nobel, Edgar Allen Poe, Gustave Flaubert, Fyodor Dostoevsky, Lewis Carroll, Theodore Roosevelt, Bud Abbott, Richard Burton, etc. ... This is only a partial list. These are, nevertheless, famous and infamous people who usually still get "oohs" and "ahhs" even after their deaths from the revelation that they were afflicted with epilepsy.

In addition to the previous list, disabled-world.com includes the following: Sir Isaac Newton, Napoleon Bonaparte, Agatha Christie, Charles Dickens, Michelangelo, Leonardo Da Vinci, George Frideric Handel, Charles V of Spain, Pythagoras, Hannibal, Hector Berlioz, James Madison, Lord Byron, Louis XIII of France, Margaux Hemingway, Martin Luther, Niccolo Paganini, Peter the Great, etc. ...

You can take this epiphany about the disability of epilepsy a giant leap forward by paradoxically going backward in time and searching the internet to inquire on an even broader level the staggering number of famous persons with epilepsy. You will come up with a generally accepted list of names ranging from religious figures to secular rulers. In between those two categories, you will also stumble on athletes, writers, composers, actors, scientists, and musicians who are thought to have epilepsy. The list will shock you. Again, you will remark, "I never knew."

On one hand, I am comforted and encouraged by the fact that so many gifted past public personalities have epilepsy, though I am sorry that they had to live with seizures. Information like this, on the other hand, brings up the deep, disturbing questions of how many other famous people suffered from seizures and desperately did what they could to hide them. The stigma was there back then. Why else would they hide a health condition? If truth be told, it is a shame since it would have been astonishing to have had outspoken role models with epilepsy.

Of course, I have my biases for role models. Did you know about St. Paul, for example? He was first named Saul and later became known as Saint Paul. Perhaps Saul was renamed Paul due to an epileptic episode. This in no way diminishes his authentic conversion to Christianity. The dramatic account is that Saul was ordered to Damascus to incarcerate Christians when he experienced a sudden, bright flash of light. He instantaneously collapsed. "Saul got up from the ground, and though his eyes were open, he could see nothing ..." (Acts 9:8) Just the details of the story alone — falling down and experiencing temporary blindness are circumstantial evidence of a seizure. Three days later, Saul converted to Christianity and went on to become one of the greatest Apostles in the church. Epilepsy, in some parts of the world, is even acknowledged as "St. Paul's Disease."

Did you know that American President Theodore Roosevelt had epilepsy? Did you know that Anglican Deacon and *Alice in Wonderland* author, Lewis Carroll also had epilepsy? Some of his images from Wonderland are believed to be seizure-influenced. In addition to these two, did you know that the Olympic sprinter Florence Griffith Joyner lived with epilepsy and died in her sleep from a tonic-clonic seizure? The seizure suffocated her. Did you know that or did you just say, "I never knew"?

Would these famous people, the living and the dead, voluntarily wear or have worn the E for epilepsy or S for seizure around their neck? Would they even get a tattoo? Would they go so far as to wear the modern Scarlet S or E of a medical alert bracelet? I wear one for pragmatic purposes. It tells my name, medical condition and gives contact information. It says something about me yet does not define me. I even turn my simple, silver medical bracelet to face you so that you can clearly make out the word "Epilepsy."

I live with a medical condition. I do not care who knows. I am an evangelist for epilepsy, as well as how God helps me to be alive with seizures.

Chapter Twenty-Nine

PHASE V - ACCEPTANCE

Embers of Acceptance

But the Lord said to him, "Peace be to you; do not fear, you shall not die." Judges 6:23

He woke up and rebuked the wind, and said to the sea, 'Peace! Be still!' Then the wind ceased, and there was a dead calm. He said to them, 'Why are you afraid? Have you still no faith?' Mark 4:39-40

Almighty God, we entrust all who are dear to us to thy never-failing care and love, for this life and the life to come, knowing that thou art doing for them better things than we can desire or prayer for; through Jesus Christ our Lord. Amen. BCP, p. 831

S ince August 2, 2009, I have been stumbling along the involuntary and convoluted path of seizures. In the pages of my journal, you can trace how certain portions of my travels with this grief have been onward.

There are, nevertheless, times when it has been simple for me to get sidetracked, stuck, stopped or just plain lost along the passageway of misfiring neurons. I would like to make some edits here to make my story more linear, but that would not be fair or honest to you and to me. My inconsistency is not only a portion of the intricacy of being human; it is a normal part of the grief journey.

Grief is not a straight line. The path is uneven, treacherous, and has unintentional detours. Yet I can glimpse some rays of acceptance up ahead for me now that the longest part of this path with epilepsy begins to emerge. I have no comprehension as to how extensive the unique phenomena called "epilepsy grief" — if there is such a thing — is going to take. With the camaraderie of family and friends, the journey moves onward; hopefully, it keeps progressing and is less lonely.

Mental Health Professionals are also guides with grief. For example, I used to meet monthly with a therapist after the time of my resection surgery. As I recently reflected on his counsel, he has helped me navigate some parts of this tandem ride of epilepsy, pedaling along with me as a professional partner in grief. In our last session, he said gently, "I want you to think about one word." Little by little through my drug-induced fog, I fought to give him my full attention. Lifting my head, he sat still while I focused on him. There was a pregnant pause. With complete clarity, he replied "Contentment" in response to my confused, quizzical look. The silence stretched, but his eyes were still engaged in the conversation. He then fixed his piercing and wise eyes onto mine with laser-like precision and spoke, "Though it's going to take some time to get there, I think you are moving toward contentment." And with that, he left the room to give me time to reside and rest in reflective silence.

Silence was the end of that session and a beginning of a new movement along the path. As I daily step forward into this invisible, still an elusive concept of contentment, I have to trust that the aforementioned will direct me toward the destination of acceptance. In the way of an addendum to his last session with me, it turns out that his words were indeed prophetic. In a sermon I preached a full year and a half after our therapy, quite "coincidentally" the theme of the sermon was ... contentment. I did not put this contentment connection together until just very recently; all along, contentment was shepherding me, a lost sheep to the green pasture of acceptance. "I shall not be in want."

Chapter Thirty

Family Ties?

A generation goes, and a generation comes ... Ecclesiastes 1:4

For the Lord is good;
his steadfast love endures for ever,
and his faithfulness to all generations. Psalm 100:5

Will you be responsible for seeing that the child you present is
brought up in the Christian faith and life?

I will, with God's help.

Will you by your prayers and witness help this child to grow
into the full stature of Christ?

I will, with God's help. BCP, p. 302

One medical fact that you might have been unaware of up until this point is that my Cavernous Malformation is more than likely a familial medical condition. My grandfather, who I never knew, had epilepsy. He died before I was born of what was diagnosed as Pick's Disease by the doctors at an infamous place in Georgia: Milledgeville. Milledgeville was created by Georgia Lawmakers in 1837 to be that asylum where epileptics and lunatics were sent. Everyone knew, without even needing an explanation, that Milledgeville was a hospital where you went to suffer and then die. If anything, undesirables were removed from the public and encaged in private.

As agonizing as this has been, hearing part of my grandfather's story through my father and uncle has led to the opening stages of acceptance. For instance, my grandfather too had seizures that occurred in church, though he was not a clergyman. He also would "space out" and then come to. He too lost his living due to his seizures. It was not uncommon for him to fall off of a ladder at his Hardware Store. Your body can only take so much. Similarly, he despised — yes, despised — his medication, which at that time was Dilantin. He simply refused to take it. He underwent brain surgery. We went through extraordinarily equivalent experiences. I go from the extreme experiences of wanting to vomit due to his pain yet beam because of his refusal to quit.

What follows is a more personal account of my epilepsy that literally fills in the blanks of a story that was just beginning to surface. I remember the first time that the descriptive features of his — my grandfather's — story began to emerge. It was in discussion with my mother while driving home from St. Simons Island, Georgia to Signal Mountain, Tennessee, in a thunderstorm somewhere along Interstate 75 North. Here is the way that I remember our conversation:

"Did anyone else in the family have seizures?" I finally asked out loud to both break the silence and satisfy my hunger and thirst for more detailed knowledge. "You already know that your dad's father did," my mother replied in a calm voice. She went into more details and continued on this time in a stronger and speedier voice, "It was always put down to a farm accident when your grandfather was a boy and living in Nebraska. He was hit so hard in the head by a swing that it knocked him out. His subsequent seizures were always blamed on the swing accident."

She pressed on while her courage was sturdy and said clearly and confidently, "From what I know about it, your grandfather worked for Sears, but his condition caused him to be passed over for promotions, so he left there to start his own hardware store in East Atlanta. He would from time to time 'blackout' and then 'come to' himself. His episodes grew progressively worse, and he hurt himself. There was a story about him showing up at the hardware store clutching a phone book and covered in scratches. It was, and always has been, a mystery as to how he got there."

I did not know what to say to all of this cloaked family history that was finally erupting from a calm surface. I had always wanted to know, but the flipped open "Pandora's Box" was a treasure trove of secrets spilling out into the open air; it was a bit more than I had bargained for. "He later died in Milledgeville," she added in a somber whisper. I knew what Milledgeville was. Milledgeville was where the State of Georgia Mental Hospital was located. When I was a kid, Milledgeville had the reputation of being the "insane asylum."

Years of silence were beginning to speak to me. I wanted to know or did I? Did I really want to know about the grandfather I never knew? This inner struggle was making me queasy, twisting my intestines almost to the point of blurting out "enough" just to make it go away. Paralyzed in this emotional twinge of pain, I balanced myself with steadying, though cleverly concealed, sips of air right there on the passenger's seat of my mom's car. I had asked for information and received it. It was that simple.

My ultimate desire for family history, not dark or scandalous, was being brought out in the open in a way that could aid me in putting together some more pieces of this grand jigsaw puzzle of not-talked-about generational neurological issues. I pressed on, "Anyone else in the family with the seizures?" Mom responded as more rain splattered the windshield, "Not one that we know of. That kind of medical information was not talked about until very recently. That's why you know so very little about family history. It's a generational thing. People back then just didn't talk about it. It's probably little consolation, George, but people are talking about epilepsy now. That's due to you in our family. That's due to people like you for the rest of society."

In his own mysterious way, my grandfather on my father and uncle's side of the family has given me some enigmatic company along this epilepsy journey. Subsequently, Edgar engaged the worst of the worst seizures. They are the ones that I am now facing: the Tonic-Clonic seizure category, also known as "Grand Mal". Again, I never knew my grandfather. But I know him better now. He died in 1961. Now 54 years later, I am getting to know him for the first time. I am not really sure why this piece of his life has helped me at all, but some inner peace is slowly beginning to sink in. Perhaps it is because another family member went through what I am going through. I feel less lonely with his company. His journey is over; mine has lasted only about six years to this point. Yet in some holy and unfathomable way, I sense that Edgar's epilepsy journey continues on, this time as my guide. I hope, with that role, he is at peace.

Though I walk through the valley of the shadow of death,
I shall fear no evil;
For you are with me;
Your rod and your staff, they comfort me.

Edgar, thank you for your company. I think, you get this, in all integrity.

Chapter Thirty-One

Wrapping it Up?

Let the peace of Christ rule in your hearts ... Colossians 3:15

Renew in these your servants the covenant you made with them at their Baptism. Send them forth in the power of that Spirit to perform the service you set before them; through Jesus Christ your Son our Lord ... BCP, p. 309

Fifty million people around the world plus George have brains that have betrayed them. We live each and every day with brains that are not like other people's brains. And through absolutely no culpability of our own. We are in different stages of grief in this sojourn we did not want. We have to make the best of our reality and live, and live every day, and live every day like the very gift it is that is given to us. Our wish is to live and give the gift of life and not merely exist. Perhaps our lives can then be a gift to you.

Children make adults look childish when it comes to this concern of living life. For instance, there are children's books that are addressing the issue that their not-quite-so-normal brains can also be a gift. They do this through the power of simple stories. This is the gist of the message that more and more books for children of diverse neurological conditions is trying to convey — their lives, their brains are gifts. They are not second class citizens or outcasts in this world. Amazing, or is it, that the children are in advance of the adults? It is both tragic and distressing to write that some adults still have a hangover from Milledgeville. That hangover continues its nauseating sway among those who get in its way. Children get sick. Adults get sick.

I think all of us, those with and without seizures, are seeking to do something as simple as and as difficult as discovering our own way in this world. The world of those with epilepsy is that we have seizures, and we live in a world that is not insular. People see us as different and sometimes as scary — we are different; our seizures can be scary. We know this. Please understand us. Please, please understand that we are striving to ascertain our way in a world where our brains have betrayed us. But we will not give up on the quest of finding our way in the world.

In the much-quoted words of Winston Churchill,

Never give up!
Never give up!
Never give up!
Never, never, never-never-never-never!

When the murkiness rolls in as you go along, the secret is being steadfast. Slowly and steadily you move and stumble, yet you continue to move even when movement is not literal. "You never give up! You never give in!" Others join you in your journey, and together you move through the haze, not sure where it will end but knowing that it is a measured time when there is unmeasured healing in the many forms it takes.

Your brain has betrayed you, but you and others can step beyond coping and surviving. You and others live with your epilepsy. Although it is living with epilepsy, it is still living and living in a different way and living, living, living with every step you take. No step is sure, but it is still living instead of being immobilized by fear thus not really living at all.

My specific circumstances as a priest are somewhat different from others with epilepsy. Priests are "supposed" to be immune from such a condition as epilepsy. Of course, this is an out-and-out bogus belief. Hopefully, this journal has let you into Father George's world. More people are beginning to know my story. They know that my clerical collar has literally been shaken within the literal context of a seizure. They know that my faith has literally been stirred by my medical condition called epilepsy but they — and now perhaps you — have encountered an imperfect man called to be a priest who has candidly shared his life and faith, warts and all, with you. I continue to move forward no matter what. I hope you will, too.

Chapter Thirty-Two

Far, Very Far, from Wrapping it Up

But I will not take my steadfast love from him ... II Samuel
7:15a

*Father, you loved the world so much that in the fullness of time
you sent your only Son to be our Savior. Incarnate by the Holy
Spirit, born of the Virgin Mary, he lived as one of us, yet without
sin. To the poor he proclaimed the good news of salvation; to
prisoners, freedom; to the sorrowful, joy.* BCP, p. 374

This priest must confess to you that the preceding
paragraph was the original conclusion of this
journal. You can read from here on out that
something significant, yes, very significant has happened
in the acceptance phase of grieving. Read on. This incident,
and the ones that follow, regrettably is a commonplace
occurrence for those suffering from seizures.

When I returned home, there were drips of messy blood on
the carpet, as well as a small, circular spot of dried urine. I

surveyed the physical evidence but denied that they were mine. Denial. Denial. Denial. Again. Again. Again. They were the remnants — the exhibit A and exhibit B — that something significant had happened to the left and side table of my bed. To add to the evidence, on my body was a light blue and white paper-like bracelet encircling my wrist. Enclosing the rest of my body, a ridiculous looking, thin and light blue begged-for jumpsuit of sorts (see page 199) was the final confirmation of proof that "it" had happened again.

The date was August 15, 2013, and the time was about 8:30 in the morning. I had just been discharged from Erlanger Hospital in Chattanooga, Tennessee. Putting these pointy puzzle pieces together in my scrambled brain, the conclusion was too nasty to comprehend. "It" had happened. I had my first-ever, tonic-clonic seizure. I was in denial about that too. The denial cycle was launched all over again.

Sometime between four and five in the morning, I had had a seizure so aggressive that it threw me out of bed, smashed my right eye into an angled, protruding corner of my nightstand and landed me on the floor where I went into the rigid tonic state and proceeded to the jerky clonic state. My tongue was slightly swollen and felt like sandpaper since I had unknowingly yet sadistically bitten into its left side without any conception of pain. I felt nothing, absolutely nothing, at that time.

My first memory of that morning, however, was of feeling something. It was an auditory, physical pain emanating out of a sharp and snappy, guttural voice almost obscenely close to my eardrum from a paramedic in the back of an ambulance asking, in my opinion, absurdly unintelligent questions: "Mr. Choyce, what is your name? What are the last four digits of your social security number? Do you know what day it is? Do you know where you are?" In addition to my first tonic-clonic seizure, I had another seizure so violent that it too sent me to the hospital via ambulance on January 4, 2014.

These uninvited questions forced themselves upon my face and then in through my ears. It was then that I felt something. It was pain, plain and simple. My head hurt. My brain, if it is medically possible since the brain itself cannot feel pain, hurt. My body was strapped down to a rocking stretcher. My eyes fixed onto the light yellow ceiling of an ambulance. My body responded simultaneously through rocking left and then jerking right in conscious movement. This is what a seizure must feel like.

Reeling and confused, the surreal situation was absurd. It bears repeating — it was a surreal situation, and it was absurd. On top of that, shame was now a part of the mix since I had lost control of my bladder. My control had been reduced to that of an infant. It all added up to my fear-filled feelings that moved back and forth in motion and in time to the acceleration jerks and erratic stops of an ambulance.

My first thoughts were simple. I just want to go back to bed, my bed and get these sterile-smelling, surgical people away from me. "All of you, you just go away," were the newborn thoughts pulsing and pounding through my head. But they were stillborn. The journey from brain to mouth is a short distance, but my thoughts died in the process and were not born into speech. My brain had just been through a grand mal seizure; my tongue was raw and red. I could not get the words "go away" to come out of my mouth anyway, even if I had wanted to.

"Go away," is what I have been saying to epilepsy since 2009, when I *can* speak. Epilepsy ignores my neurotic shriek and pitiful plea. On the other hand, I deny over and over that I have even had a seizure. How is that for a reality check? Welcome to my world. You do not want to be in this world. You can, however, leave it.

A colleague and I were talking about this very issue. She coined the idiom, "You say, 'Walk a mile in my shoes.' I retort, 'Live a day in my brain.'" It's a clever expression because it seduces you in — it did for me — and woos you into the effects of the misfiring nerves and rewiring of an epileptic's brain.

I cannot leave the misfiring of nerves and rewiring of my brain to the biology of my brain, on the other hand. I have become something or someone — I have not quite decided which — swinging between what is real and imaginary, between sanity and lunacy, between joy and despair. Epilepsy is, nevertheless, real. The fact that a seizure comes back leech-like after two years of dormancy, sucker punches me, and literally lands me on the floor is what makes this so hard to accept. This bears repeating: Epilepsy is, nevertheless, real. There is tainted, trace evidence of cleaned-up blood and urine on the carpet that could hold up in a Court of Law if I ever needed convincing.

I cannot sanitize my epilepsy journey for you. I need to write it to tell the story. You need to read it and hear the story. Life-changing is a strong expression, but writing and reading are life-changing. As so many have said to me to persuade me to put pen to paper in the form of this journal — "It is a story that needs to be told, and you need to tell it."

People need to know that epilepsy is an offensive condition. Epilepsy is a messy condition. Epilepsy is parasitic condition which I thought had run its course. The parasite has patience and in its silent slumber simply strengthened over time.

Chapter Thirty-Three

Developing Acceptance ... Again

As you therefore have received Christ Jesus as Lord, continue to live your lives in him. Colossians 2:6

a time to weep, and a time to laugh;
a time to mourn, and a time to dance; Ecclesiastes 3:4

May the Holy Spirit, who has begun a good work in you, direct and uphold you in the service of Christ and his kingdom. Amen. BCP, p. 419

Normally I would see this August 15th experience in terms of "back to square one." Although I am frustrated beyond what these words can conceivably convey, I no longer can look at epilepsy as an opponent. I am different. I am in a different place. I am not "back to square one." I think I finally came to this healthy and positive method of reflection when I titled and wrote the following article for the Southeast Tennessee Epilepsy Foundation. It is called "Some

Breakthroughs with Breakthroughs":

I think I have done just about everything right to eliminate my seizures. Isn't that our goal: eliminate or at least control seizures? I first made an appointment with my primary care physician, who after my first seizure (Complex Partial), ordered a CT scan. There was a spot on it, so he immediately sent me to a Neurosurgeon to interpret the affected area, as well as order an MRI. (Various MRIs are on pages 204-208) He diagnosed that the abnormality on both the CT and MRI was a Cavernous Malformation. He, then, described my options: surgery or medication. I went with medication that was prescribed by Dr. So-and-So, a neurologist, who is, I was told, 'the best in town.' I am sure he is. I am not questioning his competence. The issue was that the medication did not control my seizures; the Complex Partial seizures continued. It also turned out that I was allergic to the medication, which was manifested in my flesh as a relentless rash.

It was time to go to step two, which was surgery. A friend of mine, a radiologist, recommended a new surgery technique called Cyberknife and strongly suggested the facility at UAB, which was, 'the best that there is.' (This was before Erlanger Hospital had this technology.) Well, the Cyberknife surgery kind of worked. The Cavernous Malformation had shrunk yet I continued to have seizures.

I returned to step one and worked even more closely with my neurologist to find an AED combination of two prescriptions to eliminate the seizures. Again, that kind of worked. There is, however, no 'kind of worked' when it comes to seizures. It is like 'kind of pregnant.' You either are or you are not. You either have seizures or you don't.

In desperation, I went back to step two with the recommendation of another doctor friend to go to Dr. So-and-So, who is, I was told, 'the best neurosurgeon in town.' So I went to him in November of 2011 for full-blown resection to remove the entire spot deep within my left frontal lobe just above the temporal lobe that an EEG picked up as the source of my seizures. Well, that 'kind of worked' for almost two years. I had another seizure, a Tonic-Clonic this time that left me with a boxer-like black eye and an incredibly sore shoulder and arm.

Medication, surgery, more medication, more surgery; this is the litany of slow steps I have taken. And they all 'kind of worked.' But I am looking at things differently now, by having breakthroughs with breakthrough seizures, if you will. Personally, I would like to control or even eliminate seizures for they are such unpleasant experiences for me, as they are to the people who witness them. But what do I do now, knowing that I probably will have seizures for the rest of my life? What possibilities are there out there for me? To get even more specific to my situation, what are the vocational possibilities for an Episcopal priest who has uncontrolled and 'un-eliminated' seizures? It is my unique question, unless, of course, you are an Episcopal priest.

How are you going to respond to your seizures, breakthrough or regular, as a student, employee, volunteer, homemaker, retiree, etc. ...? I think that is an incredibly significant question. Is it a fight against seizures or is it an acceptance that this is our reality? If it is a fight, then what are you going to do if you 'lose' your battle to breakthrough seizures? If it is acceptance, then how are you coping now?

My breakthrough with breakthrough seizures has to do with the 'how to live now' part of the question. For instance, about a week ago I would have seen my circumstances as losing in my fight against seizures and going backward in progress. That is no longer how I think. Personally, upon deliberate reflection, I am rather proud of how far I have journeyed.

Additionally, it has not been a solitary sojourn. I am profoundly grateful for those, whether they have epilepsy or not, who have taken the epilepsy road with me. There is the physical road of thousands of miles going to hospitals, doctors, and the pharmacy. There is the emotional, grief side of the journey that is yielding to some acceptance. Finally, there is the spiritual side of the journey that I am still working through with genuine intentionality but cannot articulate just yet my spiritual breakthroughs with the integrity that I would like. These are some of my breakthroughs since my Tonic-Clonic breakthrough seizure. What are your breakthroughs about epilepsy, grief, and spiritual matters upon reading this far in my journal?

Chapter Thirty-Four

"God bless you, George"

The Lord your God turned the curse into a blessing for you, because the Lord your God loved you. Deuteronomy 23:5

See if I will not open the windows of heaven for you and pour down for you an overflowing blessing. Malachi 3:10b

Be present, O merciful God, and protect us ... so that we who are wearied by the changes and chances of this life may rest in your eternal changelessness, through Jesus Christ our Lord. Amen. BCP, p. 133

The rubber is meeting the road for this priest who wears a shaken collar and lives with a stirred faith as I persist to reflect upon my epilepsy journey. So much continues to happen. My life is changing once again, yet you are invited to come along should you desire to keep me company on the road of seizures.

Early on, I entertained the thought of the alliteration of contrasting betrayed and blessed when it came to my brain, specifically when it came to seizures. You know, B and B and B. Here is a part of my thinking:

The synonyms for blessing, according to the thesaurus on Microsoft Word, are as follows: approval, sanction, permission, go-ahead, consent, lucky thing, good thing. This was not really what I was going for when it came to writing about "being blessed by my brain." Most would understand "betrayed by my brain." Now it is time for me to dig deeper and ask, "Well, what in the world did you mean by that clever alliteration? Has this been a lucky thing or a good thing? Do any of the other synonyms accurately come close to what you are trying to express here?" I do not think that they do. And please note how far along in this journal it has taken me to get intentional and employ the word "blessing" even on an infrequent basis. It has not escaped my notice either.

Blessing carries a spiritual overtone to it. For me, blessing is a crucial step in the healing leading to acceptance. Furthermore, I cannot deny that the priest ember is beginning to glow again. Healing, acceptance, and vocation are woven together in a chaotic creation. Blessing did that. Even those of you who do not like organized religion in any form would assent that blessing carries some sort of a spiritual connotation, and you avoid saying it. You might even recoil seconds after you have sprayed the air with a sneeze and someone automatically says, "God bless you."

Let's ponder just a little while longer. So I am vehemently shaking on the floor, with blood dripping from around my eye and with the bladder control of a baby. Am I blessed? Did God bless me with epilepsy? At this point in my journal, I will let you in on a secret. I am stuck. Perhaps I can pick it up in a day or two and have a cohesive thought. For now, however, I am not actually angry anymore. There is a calmness that I do not know what to make of. Is this acceptance? Has epilepsy been a blessing? Quite candidly, I feel empty.

The beauty of a journal is that it is like we are having a conversation, albeit a one-sided dialogue. So I can let you in on the secret that it is a few days later now and I am still contemplating the word "empty." Is empty simply the opposite of being full? Is being empty acceptance? Is being empty a blessing? I am thinking that emptiness is the acceptance that epilepsy and I are going to have to make the best of it. We are living together, yet I never invited him or her or it into my brain. Radiation, excision, and medication have all failed to stop the seizures. Manage, yes. Eliminate, no.

It is almost as if I need to forgive epilepsy for the damage done. Holding onto anger is the real disease and significantly more toxic than seizures. Anger splashes through the skin and breaks into our bones. Somewhere along the conduit of skin to bone, anger slowly, seemingly cancer-like subsequently poisons everything else in its path. It even tried, in all of its arrogance, to try to poison my relationship with God. You can trace that toxin throughout this journal. Forgiveness is the antidote giving me the grace to live in the acceptance phase of grief and beyond.

I need to forgive epilepsy because it is bigger than the misfiring of neurons. Forgiveness is soul work; it goes past skin and bones and lobes of the brain into a sacred space. Anger is fed by all of the misfiring in a life well-planned that did not go as planned. The real disease is of anger that could take up permanent residence in my heart instead of the Cavernous Malformation that took up temporary residence in my brain. For too long, I have been "letting the sun go down on my anger." I think I am beginning to understand through raw experience why the Apostle Paul gave this counsel. Anger is a literal heart attack.

Though the anger portion of grief cannot be sidestepped, the effects of held-onto anger are long lasting, perhaps eternal. The spot in my brain will be burned away at cremation. The acceptance is coming to grips that life is on life's terms, not mine. Somewhere along the journey, the question of a new call in the priesthood will have to be addressed. I look forward to that but am not quite ready for such a profound question.

The brain, nevertheless, I thought betrayed me actually betrayed itself. Somewhere in that mystifying transaction, I was given an utterly unexpected gift of a blessing. The blessing is that my betraying brain is teaching me how to live. Whatever time that there is left to go in my lifetime, I will make the most of it.

Chapter Thirty-Five

Epiphany after a Big Birthday

For the Lord does not see as mortals see; they look on the outward appearance, but the Lord looks on the heart. I Samuel 16:7b

O heavenly Father, who hast filled the world with beauty: Open our eyes to behold thy gracious hand in all thy works ... BCP, p. 814

So much in these reflections in this journal of sorts has been viewed through the pitying lens of how much I have lost. The fact that I am recognizing this truth and am now working toward an approach to life that is based on gratitude for what I have and for what else is out there as opportunity, means that I am growing up into a fresh start. The people who have stayed close to me validate that I have every right to be angry since so much has been taken away. You can put it on paper and see that they are correct. Position, salary, and health are the most obvious losses. Other losses are to my sense of self-worth, my identity, my prestige in the community — and though they are impossible to quantify objectively — are nevertheless very real losses, at least they are to me.

Here's an example of this: Not long ago, I observed a former parishioner at a doctor's office. He, however, did not see me. Well, he did perceive with his eyes that there was a person in a chair in the waiting room of a doctor's office. He blankly looked right through me as if I was not even there. All the while, he was barking orders into his cell phone in a nervous-sounding, impatient voice. To be fair, I honestly do not think that he recognized me in blue jeans and a T-shirt with a "Black Dog" logo on the front. If I had had my collar on, I think the scenario would have been vastly different.

Do "clothes make the man"? In my case, this is a question of disgrace that, if the truth be known, I worshipped and bowed down to the prestige idol for years. And I have to be honest that my identity and self-worth were, to some extent, tied inexorably to my public validation from others.

Perhaps these personal epiphanies have something to do with the age odometer clicking over recently to 50. I am just happy at this point to have gotten this far, as well as for all that I still have. First, there is Anne. She is still with me. As I referred to earlier, Anne made a vow in 1985 which began In the Name of God. And she promised to stay with me

> To have and to hold from this day forward, for better for worse, for richer for poorer, in sickness and in health, to love and to cherish, until we are parted by death.

Well, those vows, particularly "in sickness and in health," have been forcefully shoved to the outer limits of their border due to seizures — my seizures. Furthermore, the portion of the marriage vows that is prior to "from this day forward," is "to have and to hold." My seizures became a part of her physical experience as Anne held me through some of my nighttime seizures. If that is not upholding the vows of marriage, then check your pulse.

Likewise, my "kids" who are now 23, 21, 19, and 16 are still with me. To be truthful and transparent, some of them had to move back home. So in that physical sense, they are still with me. More importantly, nevertheless, I mean that they are still with me since my seizures are not a source of shame for them. We even find humor in my anti-seizure medication schedule. Preston sets his cell phone alarm to 8:30 p.m. and then yells out "drug time, Dad" when the reminder rings. My children did not disavow their relationship with me either just the same as Anne did not break her marriage vow and just up and leave me. The promise of "in sickness and in health" was passed along to them through Anne's example. So they stayed and were willingly and sometimes unwillingly sucked into the whirlpool of epilepsy — my epilepsy.

Chapter Thirty-Six

The New Math of Acceptance does not Add Up

Death has been swallowed up in victory.
Where, O death, is your victory?
Where, O death, is your sting?
I Corinthians 15:54-55

Ironic, isn't it? I gained a Cavernous Malformation and gained Epilepsy; these two gains or pluses added up to a huge loss or minus or to use an accounting term, they "put me in the red." This is where the paradox fully kicks in. The minus led to immeasurable pluses or "being in the black." I have gained so much more than lost. I gained in life experiences and opportunities that have made me far richer than I ever would have been. Betrayal, ironically, led me to blessings, though not innumerable financial ones but immeasurable blessings that cannot be taken away even with shrinking resources.

So now it is time to go forward, no longer going back. Back is back to what is known and what is familiar. That is all

I wanted to do at the beginning of the epilepsy journey; to go back to what is routine, comfortable, even safe. That was my failsafe, somewhat arrogant arrangement then.

I've come too far for that now. I am different, but what I am, I am unsure of. The past sentence is filled with letter "I" three times in just a short space. The sentence before it also contains an "I". It's a bit uncomfortable to see the near narcissism revealed in those unedited sentences. Too many "I's" are grief-induced narcissism. I am not excusing here, just explaining to open a window for you into my real life. The multiple "I's" were left there purposely so that you can plainly see my myopic vision. Let my faults hold a mirror up to your face. My mirror mocks me in that silent and sarcastic voice, "Just who do you think you are, George?" I ask myself the same thing. Some of the time, my question is kind. At other times, it has a taunting tone.

Even though working through this painful process into the acceptance phase of grief, the issue of identity still looms large and then oozes out no matter how much I try to push it down. Who am I and what am I in a shaken collar and a stirred faith? Identity issues even came out when I recently had a rare chance to preach. It was only after rereading the sermon text that it struck me that my identity pain was coming out in public. I decided not to "oomph" up the sermon or even edit it for this journal. Here is a portion of a sermon preached on Sunday, September 29th, 2013, at the Episcopal Church of the Annunciation in New Orleans, Louisiana:

> There came a point in the darkest days of disability that I basically forced myself to go

to church. Though I did *not know* what or how much I believed, I did *know* that one place where I could feel God was at church. Sometimes I sat anonymously alone in the back pew in a puddle of silent, salty tears. I had on a coat and tie so no one knew who or what I was. I did not know who or what I was anymore, for that matter.

Where do you go from the back pew of the church? You go out. You cannot stay in the sanctuary of the sanctuary. You must move. You are fortunate even to move forward. A friend of mine said it in this clear-cut manner — "Hey, bro, you're alive." I am quiet after that.

Forward is forward and crossing over into new territory and into the land of change. Though change brings with it the excitement of opportunity, change is still scary. But who said anything about there being a guarantee that this life is supposed to be free from fear and safe?

Though I am learning about the unsafe risk involved in this life, this life still remains a gift. I did nothing to bring myself into this world. Moreover, what I have come to believe through my foray into the feral spaces of the seizure desert is that new life bursts forth in the midst of the mounting decay of so many little deaths. Something has to die. Something has to change. Something blooms. Death and change merge and new life emerges. An Easter Lily perhaps.

Chapter Thirty-Seven

Seeing through Seizures Even if it's not What We Want to See

God is our refuge and strength, a very present help in trouble.
Psalm 46:1

... to comfort all who mourn ... Isaiah 61:2a

Give to us, your servants, that peace which the world cannot give, so that our minds may be fixed on doing your will ...
BCP, p. 123

"And they all lived happily ever after."

The above is the conclusion of the Disney movies and fairy tales that I grew up with as a child. Those of you, who have watched Disney movies, and others similar, know exactly what I am writing about. There is almost always the crashing climax of a fight scene or the poignant portrayal of a great calamity when someone supposedly dies. I am not going to name them. You probably have a vibrant mental image of mermaids, and then a rendering of unlikely animal friends, and for that matter, a further illustration of unlikely human friends. The scene then resolves itself in a gush of gooey sentiments. It really is pretty pathetic when you reflect back on it. The basic message was that good always overcomes bad; love conquers all; if at first you don't succeed, try, try again, etc.

Those endings, while entertaining and "feel good," are utterly simplistic. They are cartoons after all. While simple is fine, simplistic is not a positive word in my vocabulary. The analogy here can be the comparison of childlike to childish. Childlike is that kid who is good and trusting; childish is the kid who is bad and a brat. "Child" is a part of both expressions, yet they are chasms apart in meaning.

Life is not really that straightforward. Wish that it was, but it's not. Let me give you some alarmingly innovative, though thought-provoking, illustrations that transform cartoon storylines into a vast, disturbing dose of reality. For example, I've never seen an old-fashioned cartoon character have a seizure or much less dare to speak the word "Epilepsy." Perhaps you have, but I have missed it.

And what about this — does Donald Duck contract pancreatic cancer and lose his feathers due to chemotherapy? Is Mickey Mouse confined to a wheelchair due to injuries from an automobile accident paralyzing him from the waist down? Does Minnie Mouse face discrimination at work all because she's a mouse? Now that's real life. And I get it; I ruined some of your childhood images of some of your favorite cartoon characters. Fling this book at the wall if it helps.

At some point early on in our lives, somewhere in our soul "and they all lived happily after" took root, and something grew. What was it that grew? Was it naivety? Those of us who bear the emotional scars from living enough life would sneer and state with complete clarity, "You know, sometimes stuff just happens. And there's not a thing you can do about it." And you know what? It doesn't make for a good movie ending. And you know what? It doesn't make for a good book ending either. And you know what? It is honest. And honesty grows out of the smelly soil of manure. Conceivably this is where I will grow the most — in the muck of reality that cannot hide the scars of life.

I cannot hide the surgery scar on my forehead for much longer. The epiphanies at 50 come with a cosmetic cost. My hair continues to recede. The tarnished shower drain and the curved sides of the sink oval are the exhibits "A" and "B" in my court of reality that follicles don't lie. So I try to trick both judge and jury in that imaginary courtroom. I use, as some say, "product" in my hair. The name brand shampoos, the organic conditioners, the gels or sprays or mousse just cannot do what they all used to do. The surgery scar is emerging, little by little, year after year. The mirror makes me plainly face what is to come.

Here again is a possibility to reimage what is going on. So here goes: I, like Harry Potter, have a scar on my forehead. His was brought about from a curse when he was just a baby. My emerging scar as an adult is the literal scar on my forehead from sterile surgery. I did, however, receive a blessed mark on my forehead when I was just a baby. You cannot see it. It is there, nevertheless. The vertical and horizontal mark from the beams of the cross was traced in the blessed oil of baptism called Chrism. It was a blessed mark; not a cursed scar. I would need blessings when other scars from seizures would continue to curse me along the way. The journey was about to get messy once more.

Anne informed me this morning that I had had another seizure in my sleep three hours earlier at about 5:30. It was not vicious enough to throw me out of bed, but it still was violent. No wonder I felt so awful as if I had been through a scrap with a much more muscular opponent. The antagonist, of course, had beaten me up. The scar this time — not to be gross — was on my tongue; yes, my tongue. I had bitten down so hard on it during the seizure that it had bled. It had left its mark, though not a blessed one.

Maybe the acceptance phase is simply knowing that things may not ever get any better medically and ACCEPTING that as a lifelong reality. I may never drive again. I may always take medication and always be somewhat disconnected from my environment. I may always have to wear the bracelet that has the fading word "Epilepsy" in black letters written on a scratchy silver setting of jewelry. In fact, I need to order a new Medical Alert bracelet before the word "Epilepsy" is unreadable. My first seizure was more than five years ago. Through this journal you have journeyed with me, though not quite in a linear line, all five of those years. Can you believe that?

I shared my story, in quite a halting voice, of the experience of my nocturnal seizure with a trusted colleague this morning just five hours after it happened. I held nothing back even when it came in a combination of bits and spurts of sanity interspersed with bewilderment; all the while he listened. That is important. This sounds so, so simple, but it is not. In these uncomfortable times of puzzlement, people want to offer up simplistic, quick clichés:

1. It's always darkest before the dawn;
2. Tough times don't last but tough people do;
3. In every cloud, there's always a silver lining.

They do this to break the awkward tension.

On behalf of almost all of those who have seizures, please just listen to us. Walk with us. Don't leave us. Don't try to fix us. Something will happen.

Here is what happened to me: My colleague pastorally spoke out when I talked myself into silence just after I had shared my fear about the future of my vocation as a priest who lives with epilepsy. I think that that was and is the crux of my fear. He calmly breathed, "You are Quasimodo to them. You are different. You frighten them because you remind them that their lives are not under control. It comes down to this — they do not know what to do with you as a priest who has epilepsy." I was not expecting that response at all; nevertheless, I respected it. Furthermore, I accepted it. He has always been completely and brutally honest, though in a paradoxically compassionate manner.

His words are still sinking in. Even at this infant stage, his blunt counsel is ironically emotionally medicinal and healing. I think that that is so much a part of this acceptance phase. Oh, I will waver. This latest seizure has shaken me, literally. Frankly, I feel exhausted on the physical, emotional, and spiritual level. Those who have had seizures understand exactly, exactly what I am writing. I will not edit or sugarcoat it for you. This might turn out to be a blessing to you, as it has been to me, that this journey has been so candid.

Thank you for listening by reading. Thank you for walking with me by reading. Thank you for entering the world of those who have epilepsy by reading this journal. You have given to me the gift of grieving myself all the way up to the acceptance phase of grief over nearly five years, for that is how long it has taken me to complete this as-of-yet-completed work. This work is almost over, but the grief work of Denial, Anger, Bargaining, Depression and Acceptance will last a lifetime. Acceptance means, in the words of Robert Frost, I still have "miles to go before I sleep, and miles to go before I sleep" from the poem "Stopping by Woods on a Snowy Evening." And that's okay with me even when I am not well. I have accepted that.

Accepting acceptance requires integrity; consequently, I need to be honest with you here, again. It is as if this book is my written confession. It is as if you are the priest, my priest. This sojourn along this path to acceptance is not going to be painless or brief. To forge onward will entail ache and time. The acceptance journey continues on in ways that I could never have imagined by the seemingly insignificant items that crop up in ordinary ways in my life. I am embarrassed to put this story down, but it exposes how many miles and miles and miles to go before I sleep.

For example, my daughter asked if she could borrow some of the CT scans and MRI images from pre and post-surgery to show to her Psychology class. To tell you the truth, I was flattered that images of my brain were to be shown to a college-level psychology class. All of my epilepsy medical images and paperwork I keep under my bed. Getting on my knees, a sort of spontaneous prayer sprang up as I thanked God that I was still alive. Seeing medical images will do that to you; well, it did to me anyway.

In the midst of the medical stacks of paper was a green folder that simply did not fit the context. After swabbing off two years of chalk-like dust with a flip flopping action of my wrist, I discovered that it was a folder that had written on the front of it "Past Ministry" and "Future Ministry Possibilities." In disgust, I almost threw it away right then and there. I could not. I had to take a look inside.

In that folder, a number of attractive letters and professional stationery stared back at me. There was a curious, contradictory combination of "we invite you to consider St. So and So's Episcopal Church" to "thanks, but no thanks" stationery.

One such letter contained the following: "After a period of research into nominations and suggestions from across the country, our bishop has forwarded your name to us and suggested we invite you into this discernment. While we do not know a great deal about each other yet, we are encouraged by Bishop So and So's recommendation as we set out to do our initial work of invitation and screening."

Another letter was more traditional in protocol. It stated, "We invite your prayers as to whether God may be calling you to be considered in this ministry." This one, nonetheless, was from a large and prosperous Cathedral where the attractive letterhead bore my name underneath it. The letter was requesting that I give my assent to being a part of their search process for a new Dean. A loose definition of a Dean of a Cathedral is typically the chief cleric on a large staff.

Both of these churches, and others like them, came to me in 2010 and 2011. In 2012, after my surgery, there were no invitations. That's right. Not one. This time, I was the one who entered the search discernment processes through my initiation. Every "thanks, but no thanks" letter, which was, by the way, much less attractive than the invitation letters, all conveyed the same message:

1. They appreciated my interest.

2. They reviewed my profile, and it was not selected to go any further in the process.

3. They appreciated "the time and interest you (I) invested in this process and the gifts of ministry that you (I) bring."

4. They encouraged me to contact them in the future.

5. "My prayers and blessings continue to remain with you as you continue your ministry."

One of these "thanks, but no thanks" communications arrived April 5, 2013, and was not even a letter but was sent to the inbox of my computer "Via Email." Ouch. And then to rub their Louisiana bayou salt into these Tennessee wounds, it read "Our Search Committee has not made a call and has elected to re-start the discernment process. You are welcome to participate again, but at this time the Search Committee did not discern a call for you to become our rector."

One of the last lines was "May God bless you and your ministry." But what was my ministry? And what was my, as I wrote on my green folder, future ministry? How was I ever going to find out unless I entered into an official search process?

These letters I took out one by one and spread them out over the bed. As I intentionally reflected upon and processed them on top of the comforter with my knees on the floor in a paradoxical prayer position, I moved a pillow that was on the floor to another spot. At that precise pinprick in time, as I shifted ever so slightly to my right, my knees were in the exact location where the undetectable remnants of the secret stain from my violent seizures had once commingled. It was a consecrated moment. Time stopped. Something clicked. My knees were reset in a fresh and profound position of prayer. The roots of some sort of acceptance of the grieving stage of Acceptance began to dig deeper through that physical, emotional, and spiritual stain.

Yes, epilepsy had left its immeasurable mark on me both emotionally and spiritually, as well as a measurable mark on my forehead. It has been incalculable to quantify epilepsy's effects, but "Past Ministry" was finally in the past. "Past Ministry" paperwork was and is an offering to God. Maybe it is time to burn them as a symbolic way to send the smoke heavenward so that God can do whatever with them. On the other hand, it might be better to keep them as a stark reminder in black, white, and different colors of what was once so important to me.

To be redundant here, there still lies ahead of me "Future Ministry Possibilities," which I too offer to God. My struggle is that I do not know how to do it without the modus operandi method. This reflection is something that another priest, with the disability of Lyme disease, has also given his "Amen" to: for years we served as clergy in the Church we love and now we're "out of sight, out of mind." As a disabled priest, I am going into new territory here that the Institutional Church does not discourage; it simply has no system to engage in facilitating my finding "Future Ministry Possibilities" in a formal way.

"Future Ministry Possibilities" keep manifesting themselves in the mundane everyday stuff of life. For instance, the 1991 Volvo 240 wagon one of my sons drives was showing its age; sounding its age would be more accurate. The middle muffler was no longer doing its job of muffling noise. Let me put it this way — it was quite apparent when he was driving home from any venture. Let me put it another way — it was quite apparent when he was coming home late from any venture.

Something had to be done. That is one fact we both agreed on. In a state of anxiety, he and I took the wagon to a shop that could take the vintage Volvo right away and install a generic muffler for $90. Now that is a great deal for a Swedish Wagon. We took the raucous-sounding wagon down to the garage in 15 minutes and irritated many on the way. To be honest here, I kind of enjoyed it. Well, he drove while I rode. And true to his word, the owner of the shop did what he said over the phone they would do; they took his wagon into one of the service bays straight away.

We sat in the waiting room and picked up dated magazines smudged with a creepy combination of grimy motor oil and hygienic baby wipes. Mechanics and moms bonded their worlds in the pages of those aged magazines. The slippery, slimy amalgamation on the page edges was the unanticipated and unknown creation. Realizing what that foul and congealed concoction on the edges of the pages was, I instantaneously flung the soiled magazine back onto the table. It did a "360" on other slimy, messed up magazines. As I flipped my fingers back and forth on my T-shirt to try to clean them, a slow series of "whap, whap, whap," slapping sounds invaded the nearly-empty mechanic's parking lot from the jam-packed street.

Chapter Thirty-Eight

Cavernous Malformation Continues

Where can I go from your spirit? Or where can I flee from your presence? Psalm 139:7

O God, who wonderfully created, and yet more wonderfully restored, the dignity of human nature: Grant that we may share the divine life of him who humbled himself to share our humanity, your Son Jesus Christ; who lives and reigns with you, in the unity of the Holy Spirit, one God, for ever and ever. Amen. BCP, p. 214

The thumping reverberation was emanating from the rear passenger wheel of a Ford pickup truck. From its rust spots and faded paint, it could probably tell some stories. A man and a woman got out. With hands on hips and facing their Ford, they simply stared at the shredded tire. As a mechanic from the shop approached them, they sheepishly turned in unison to face him. I recognized them immediately. They were parishioners who still went to my former Church. I did not exactly know how to behave in that moment. It was an uncanny instance though not wholly uncomfortable. Should I stand inside and hope that the tire is fixed outside? Should I go out to meet them? What should I do?

That moment was sort of a "litmus test" of the Acceptance phase of grief. I strode towards the Waiting Area door and then out into the Parking Lot. There was a split second when the woman recognized me, and slowly we walked towards one another and met halfway between their truck and the Waiting Room door. Yes, I know. Meeting halfway really is symbolic, isn't it?

What happened next in the midst of the pleasantries being exchanged was absolutely astonishing. Casual Conversation gave way to Cavernous Malformation conversation. The woman continued on and said to me sympathetically, "George, I know you can commiserate with this because it has to do with the brain and tumors." At this point, the conversation was abruptly altered to an evocative, emotional state. She blurted out despairingly, "It's about a friend of ours. You see, we have this friend we are praying for now. Well, really lots of people throughout the country and from around the world are praying for her. She's got something called a Cavernous Malformations. They are rare from what I have read about them." She plunged on with a combination of a question and a comment. "That's not what you had, was it? It couldn't have been. You look fine and she's dying from hers!"

I do not know how much time passed with this revelatory information and my stuttered "yes" to her query. The exclamation point at the end of "she's dying from hers" began to shriek of the desperation of her situation. In short, her friend's Cavernous Malformation was in her brainstem. It really is a death sentence. Her doctor sent her to a rehabilitation center because there was nothing more he could do for her. There was no more to be done other than rehabilitation and prayer. "Go home and enjoy your family," was his practical counsel. End of story, right?

Within a day, I was on the email chain prayer list. The nationwide and worldwide group had all of the medical information and went into full-swing prayer mode.

At the bottom of the email chain — remember that it has gone all across the country and possibly the world — was the name of the "scribe" of these messages, as well as her business address. Her business address was an unembellished, literal ten-minute drive from my house. Ten minutes! We're talking about seven miles. Seven miles!

I would need to gather together all of my no-nonsense Cavernous Malformation information together, along with my personal medical paperwork authenticating my Cavernous Malformation condition (See pages 209-210). While searching under the bed once more — this time for my personal medical records — Anne inquired of me what was going on. After I stood up, I conveyed to her the story that I am writing to you. She listened. She thought. She acted, thank God because I seemed incapable of proceeding any further. Most practically, Anne joined me on the floor to pull out from under the bed my personal medical paperwork to make copies on our home copier.

I would undoubtedly need the documentation when I went over unannounced to the scribe's office and said, "You don't know me from Adam, but ..."

That is exactly what happened: Pulling my car into the parking lot to find her office, I half-wished that I would not locate it. That gutless idea died out as something like a powerful, purposeful courage from outside of myself took me over; positively inundating me, if you will. Taking in a deep breath, I gathered up all of my emotional audacity, as well as the medical paperwork into a neat pile and swung my legs out of my car. Pushing the door closed with a quiet thump, I took another deep breath and strode resolutely across the parking lot to the office door.

Pushing on the glass office door, the faux doorbell chimed announcing my presence. "May I help you," a woman stated in a professional, sincere tone about five seconds after my arrival. Stammering just a bit, I responded, "I'm looking for Barbara Brown." Curving all eight of her fingers towards her shoulders and lifting her eyebrows, she breathed one word —"Me." Taking another deep gulp of air into my lungs, and then in an unsteady voice, I spoke these precise words — "You don't know me from Adam, but my name is George Choyce and I, like your friend, have a Cavernous Malformation. Well, I had one. It's gone now."

She stared at me with utter incredulity and complete astonishment. I did not know how to take this. Her eyes flitted side to side as if she was silently thinking, "OK, where's the camera?" I still could not get a read on her. Was she going to call the police, or was she going to hug me? Deciding that it would be prudent not to discover the outcome of either possibility, I instantly produced two pages of certified paperwork with my name and Cavernous Malformation in print among the meticulous medical terminology of the contents.

Taking the paperwork into her steady hands, she quickly, though confidently glanced up and down the sheet. "There and there," I muttered almost silently while pointing to "George Choyce" and "Cavernous Malformation" or "Cavernoma." I was on the precipice of pulling out my driver's license to authenticate my identity when she invited me into her office. In other words, she had decided that she did know me from Adam.

Her office was very neat yet filled with stacked packing boxes. The ones that were already assembled bore Smyth's name. My eyes ambled to every corner of the office. "We've boxed up Sam Smyth's office stuff and are sending it on to him in South Carolina," she interjected to reply to my quizzical look. She then motioned me over to the desk with a relaxed wave of her hand. I understood this to mean that she trusted me. She took me at face value — a guy she did not know until five minutes ago who said he once had a Cavernous Malformation and who now just wanted to help her friend.

"Here," I added while taking out a business card that I had scribbled on with some rudimentary information about Cavernous Malformations. Adding my cell phone number to the card, I said earnestly, "have them call me if they need anything." "And here's Sam's cell phone number," she piped up. "I know he would want you to have it."

All of the information had been exchanged. There was sudden stillness, but it was not awkward. It was just one of those moments that go beyond a factual description. There was no sense of the actual amount of time that had passed; possibly it was a second or a minute or something in-between. Whatever amount of time passed, it was a sacred time, nothing more and nothing less.

Chapter Thirty-Nine

Acceptance? Still Miles to Go.

"See, I am making all things new," says the Lord. Revelation 21:5

Kairos time is accurate. It means God's timing to make something extraordinary ensue. On the other hand, Chronos or chronological time is a more ordinary and literal time as relating to the tyranny of clock or calendar. To use a slang and religious expression, it was a "Godincidence." Here's what I mean: It was just a coincidence that my friends had a flat tire, right? It was just a coincidence that due to my friendship with them that I got on the email chain, right? It was just a coincidence that the bottom of the email contained the address of the "scribe" which was just down the mountain from me, right? I hope your response is something like a sarcastic sounding, "Yeah, right. Just a coincidence." If not that previous response, I hope it is something like, "It is a Godincidence."

At the time of this writing, the woman is recovering in South Carolina, as well as finishing up some medical treatment in Florida to be strong enough to travel. If both of these medical treatments are successful, she will have the opportunity to fly out to Arizona to have the surgery she needs to remove the Cavernous Malformation from her brainstem. You know, in some mysterious and mystical connection through her medical condition, she has given a gift to me. And she does not even know it. The bottom line is that she knows what it is like to have a Cavernous Malformation.

While I have received an amazing amount of support, it is from family and friends. They do not have a Cavernous Malformation. What I mean is that they do not know, for the most part, what it means to have something in your brain that is not supposed to be there in the first place. And that that something in your brain could hemorrhage — sending blood violently splattering in all directions. Yes, it is a gory description. I know it is. These hemorrhages have killed people and sorely wounded others. When my Cavernous Malformation hemorrhaged, it gave me epilepsy.

The exception to family and friends not knowing how a Cavernous Malformation affects me is Anne. We go to sleep at night together. We wake up in the morning together. We go through life together. As we have spent 29 years together in marriage and two years before that as we dated, we got to know one another. I wrote previously, "Anne just gets me." She knows that this Cavernous Malformation in my head, well, the Cavernous Malformation that used to be there and the area surrounding it where blood has splattered, wreaks havoc with your psyche and soul. She knows that, from time to time, three centimeters that used to be in my brain continues to wreak havoc on George Choyce's soul. It gets personal because it is.

To continue my reflection about the gift the woman with the Cavernous Malformation has given me, I essentially know her name and have read some, just some, of her story via some e mails. Even she does not "know me from Adam," but that does not really matter. All she knows is that some guy from Signal Mountain in Tennessee took the time to go see one of her friends in Chattanooga and share his story. The geographic arrows are pointing all over the map. The woman who lives in South Carolina and has received medical treatment in Florida will go to Arizona to have surgery to remove her Cavernous Malformation has ministered, if you will, to a guy in Tennessee who now is less lonely in his journey through the grief stages brought on by a Cavernous Malformation he used to have. That's the gist of it. That's the gift in it.

This is my story, but it is also your story. Those of you who have lost something significant or someone special to you have experienced grief in a visceral manner. It is, or it was a journey that was thrust upon you. You did not choose it. The phases of grief — Denial, Anger, Bargaining, Depression, Acceptance — are a path that anyone who is grieving must, yes, must, take either willingly or unwillingly to get healthy.

This book is about to conclude. My shaken collar and my stirred faith, wait and wonder where the blessing of my brain will blossom and into what. There are more questions than answers still. Where will it take me and the others who have taken this journey — some willingly and others not-so-willingly? When will this be? What will that be? I do not know precisely. Of course, for a guy who is impatient, this lack of control is beyond wearisome. What I do know is that there will be new life. This priest might even use the Biblical vocabulary of "resurrection" to express the experience of exponentially moving forward in the steps of the Acceptance phase in the grief process.

God knows that I want to give you the "and they all lived happily ever after" ending to optimize the effect of the word "resurrection". I wanted you to think or say, "That guy has been through it, but at least the book has a happy ending with no loose ends." I cannot do that. It lacks integrity. To write less than honestly literally lacks honesty; furthermore, it would insult those grieving the loss of something or someone significant. The ending will, nevertheless, impart some final hope for you to hang on to.

I want you to consider this coming-to-a-close image: Even though Jesus was truly raised from the dead, maybe his clothes were not beautifully bleached robes of crisp white linen material upon his bursting forth from the dank and dark tomb. Maybe Jesus was still adorned in his gray, grave clothes. Maybe it was not the dazzling, luminous Jesus we were expecting. Jesus, nevertheless, was raised from the dead; it's just that it was not in the way we had pictured or in the way we were expecting. In like manner, new life through grief will arise but not in the way we were anticipating. Once we can believe this, we can accept anything else that comes our way, which it surely will.

As I finish this journal, I pray that we will not finish our journey. Let me put this into context for you. As I write this, it is extremely early on the morning of December 5, 2014. I am looking out over the front yard as a moist mist oppressively obscures the woods of Cool Springs Road, knowing that one end will be coming, knowing that one beginning will be coming, knowing that we will be moving. It truly is the Gospel — death and resurrection. Perhaps this is even what the commencement of the dim light of the resurrection from the tomb resembled. From my vantage point, four faint, yellow, miniature light bulbs from the front porch's two lamps feebly throw out weak illumination into the gray haze. The glow falters, yet resides, in the murkiness.

But birds are out there. I can hear them even this early. There is life out there. I do not know what it is. That bona fide image of the woods is the allegorical image for my brain. Once more, there is life out there. And once more, I do not know what it is at this precise pinprick in time and place. You see, I am up early this morning because I had another strong series of seizures just hours ago and cannot get back to sleep. I sit here typing as the fog, little by little, breaks. Way, way out there, I am beginning to see hope. Do you see it yet?

My collar has been shaken; my faith has been stirred. I am changing. I have miles and miles to go on this journey. But I made it to another day when I climbed out of bed this morning being accompanied by hope to move into the unknown — whatever, whenever, and wherever that may be. I have accepted Acceptance. And the Potter is not finished yet.

For an in-depth definition of all of these categories, please consult professional resources like those from the Epilepsy Foundation. Below is my uncomplicated understanding of seizures.

What is a Seizure?

A seizure is the rapid increase of abnormal electrical activity in the brain.

Medical classifications of seizures that fall into two groupings:

(I.) Partial and (II.) Generalized.

Partial Seizures, which occur in one part of the brain, are further divided up into simple and complex:

Simple Partial Seizures

The difference is that with the Simple Partial Seizure there is no loss of consciousness but definitely feeling odd with physical symptoms like twitching or nausea.

Complex Partial Seizures

Complex Partial Seizures are, as the name implies, far more complex in their manifestation. For example,

Complex Partial seizures can include aimless activities like picking at clothing or lip smacking. The other mannerisms that sometimes occur are that the person just stops and stares for no reason whatsoever. This category is the first manifestation of my epilepsy. It happened while I was preaching.

Generalized Seizures happen deep within the brain and then spread. Generalized seizures have five categories that are listed below. Most people think of a seizure when they witness one of these five seizures.

Absence Seizure

The first Generalized Seizure is called an Absence Seizure, which actually sounds like "ob sonce" to me. It is commonly known as a Petit Mal seizure. It lasts about 30 seconds at the most in which the person is unresponsive and sometimes twitches.

Generalized Tonic-Clonic Seizure

The second Generalized Seizure is known as Generalized Tonic-Clonic. This is the type of seizure that most people think of when they hear the word seizure or the expression epileptic fit or Grand Mal seizure. There is a tightening of the muscles, tongue biting, and rhythmic contraction of the muscles. This is the kind of seizure that sent me to the hospital twice and that I continue to have.

Atonic Seizure

The third Generalized Seizure is called the Atonic Seizure, which manifests itself with the loss of muscle tone and results in the person falling down.

Myoclonic Seizure

The fourth Generalized Seizure is called the Myoclonic Seizure. These are very brief resulting in the twitching of a certain group of muscles.

Tonic Seizure

The final Generalized Seizure is known as the Tonic Seizure. This classification of seizure lasts unusually less than 20 seconds and involves a stiffening of the muscles. Usually happens when a person is asleep. Some of the time this classification of seizure happens to me.

What is a Cavernous Malformation or a Cavernoma?

Please consult medical resources for the formal definition of a Cavernous Malformation or Cavernoma.

A Cavernous Malformation or Cavernoma is a cluster of nerves filled with blood byproducts. They resemble a raspberry in shape and look like a raspberry in color due to the blood. Bottom line — it is not supposed to be there in the first place. Most of the time, they are harmless. Some of the time, they will hemorrhage and blood will be forced out in all directions causing an irritation of the surrounding area. This often results in seizures.

The next picture is of Kelly and me upon our return from the Emergency Room of Erlanger Hospital on the morning of August 15, 2013. It was my first, of uncounted, tonic-clonic seizures.

8 Episcopal Journal September 2013

A journey with epilepsy

Reclaiming my priestly call after a debilitating disability

I was preaching one August Sunday in 2009 when to my embarrassment I lost my place in the sermon. My perception of the event was that approximately 10 seconds had passed, but in reality, I was told, it was at least one and a half minutes. I had just experienced my first seizure and had begun my reluctant journey toward disability. As a first line of defense, I passed the whole episode off with humor. "The sermon was so boring," I chuckled, "that even the preacher fell asleep." It was not funny when it happened in the pulpit again just one month later. I am an Episcopal priest, living with the disability of a seizure disorder called epilepsy. Though my story about disability is my own, it has some similarities with those of other clergy who are also living with disability. It is our own struggle for clergy wellness. There is the obvious physical side to wellness. It includes, but is not limited to, going to numerous doctors' appointments, availing oneself of physical therapy, undergoing surgery and taking medications hourly. For instance, I have a primary care physician, a neurosurgeon and a neurologist. My medications have included two high-powered AEDs (antiepileptic drugs) that were accompanied by two pages of warnings about nasty side effects. I've also had two neurosurgeries. But wellness goes significantly beyond the physical; it also includes multifaceted emotional components. I have had the pastoral care of my bishop, George D. Young III of the Diocese of East Tennessee, a therapist, and a priest from East Carolina with whom I have a weekly telephone appointment. I have also talked with Barbara Ramnaraine, a deacon at the Episcopal Disabilities Network in Minneapolis, who has been a remarkable source of both encouragement and education. However, finding other Episcopal clergy living with disabilities in order to share experiences has been an exercise in futility due to the privacy regulations of the Health Insurance Portability and Accountability Act. This separation from one another diminishes our health. Do not underestimate the depressing influence that isolation brings to our complex journey toward wellness.

There is another example of separation: think about diocesan conventions, where so often the seating plan singles out clergy who are not associated with a parish; they are seated with other onlookers or stand around the periphery of the event. Though not excluded from the Eucharist, they are unintentionally excluded from another kind of table fellowship. For me the hardest part of healing is spiritual and vocational. I went from being the rector of St. Timothy's at Signal Mountain, Tenn., to wearing my "civies" to other Episcopal churches. Clean, crisp vestments that once hung in the church's vesting room were now hanging in the closet, permeated with a musty, mothball smell. I placed my clerical collar on my dresser as an "outward and visible sign" of my priestly vocation, because sometimes I did not know who or what I was anymore. I experienced a depth of despair, difficult for others to understand, as my identity was being stripped away by my disability.

I had to find a way to climb out of despondency but found I could not do it alone. The reclaiming of some of my priestly call came when the pity party ended, and I began to consider the possibility of something new emerging in my priestly call through the workings of the Holy Spirit. I needed others who would take the time to walk with me and, even though it was awkward at first, I began to reach out to colleagues.

Another significant step in reclaiming my priestly identity came in a serendipitous moment on Christmas Eve. Entering the narthex of St. Peter's in Chattanooga with my family, the Rev. Carter Paden III spotted me and, with a huge grin, asked, "You want to 'suit up'?" I turned to my spouse with a questioning look. She nodded, then in a quiet yet clear voice said, "Go on." I needed her permission. She had walked the journey with me and had every right to be involved in the decision. It was now time for me to be at the altar again, even though I still have epilepsy. The "outward and visible sign" of my vocation, my clerical collar, is coming off the dresser and going back around my neck again as I continue to regain my identity.

I cannot emphasize enough how other Episcopalians have a profound part in our healing when it feels that our dignity has been stripped from us, and in our nakedness of disability we are unintentionally separated from the church that once called us to exercise our gift of priesthood. We clergy who are on disability offer our gift of weakness to the church, to be a visible symbol of the wounded Christ in a world filled with millions of people living with disabilities. In the broadest interpretation of the word, you can "call" us to come back and participate. And in so doing, we can begin to explore a new call in the context of our community, the Episcopal Church. After all, calls to ministry are best discerned through the community.

The Rev. George L. Choyce lives in Signal Mountain, Tenn., in the Diocese of East Tennessee.

This is the article I submitted for The Episcopal Journal, September 2013.

The following pictures are MRIs of my brain with medical descriptions that follow.

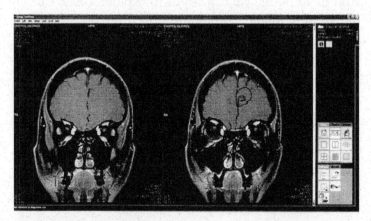

MRI Sept 2009 Prior to cyberknife

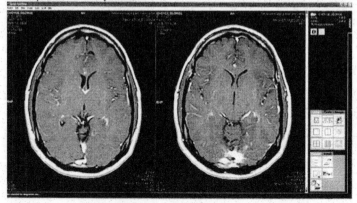

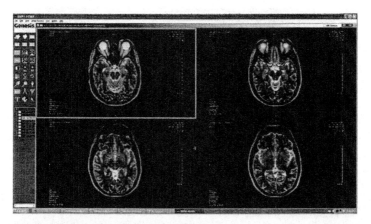

MRI SEPT 2009 prior to cyberknife

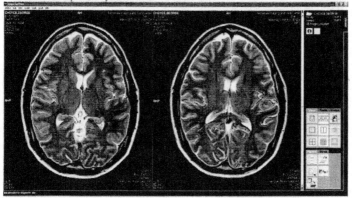

MRI Sept 2009 prior to cyberknife

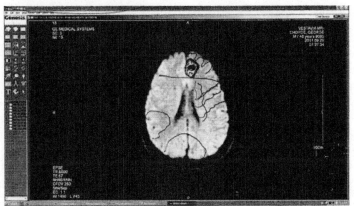

Sag T1 2011 after cyberknife

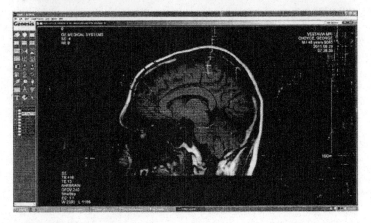

2011 Ax T2 after cyberknife

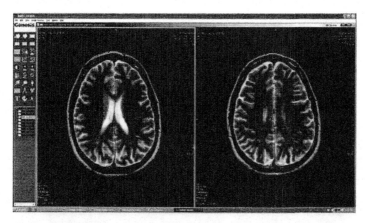

2011 Ax T1 after cyberknife

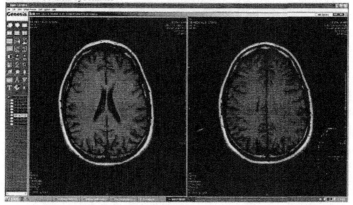

2011 Ax T1 with contrast after cyberknife

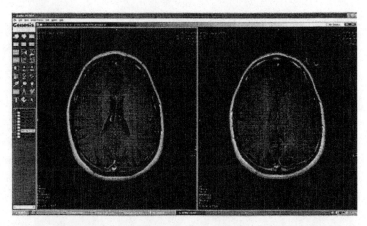

2011 Coronal T1 with contrast after cyberknife

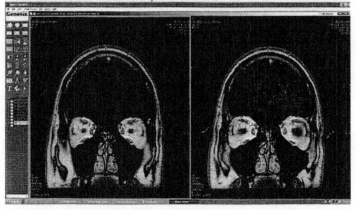

2011 Axial T2 after cyberknife. I don't see any mesial temporal sclerosis

*** Final Report ***

Exam: MRI BRAIN W/WO CONTRAST   Date of Exam: 09/08/2009

IMPRESSION: LEFT FRONTAL LOBE PROBABLE CAVERNOUS MALFORMATION/CAVERNOMA WITH A SMALL ADJACENT DEVELOPMENTAL VENOUS ANOMALY/VENOUS ANGIOMA AS DETAILED BELOW.

Reason: LEFT FRONTAL BRAIN LESION

HISTORY: Seizures and left frontal lobe lesion identified on a recent CT exam, now for characterization.

Comparison: None.

Technique: Echo-planar DWI with ADC map, axial T2 * GRE, axial FLAIR, axial T2 TSE, and multiplanar pre-/postcontrast T1 SE sequences of the brain using 20 ml of Magnevist.

Findings: Subcortical focus of magnetic susceptibility signal within the left frontal lobe white matter suggesting a cavernous malformation/cavernoma ("occult" vascular malformation, not visible on conventional angiography) particularly given the a small adjacent enhancing developmental venous anomaly/venous angioma. No adjacent associated parenchymal edema or mass effect, typical of this well documented vascular malformation association.

No abnormal DWI or additional intracranial signal abnormality. Postcontrast images reveal no abnormal brain, dural, or cranial nerve enhancement. No signal abnormality within the paranasal sinuses, middle ears, or mastoid antra. The cervicomedullary junction is normal. No focal marrow signal abnormality. The pituitary gland, orbits, and aerodigestive tract are unremarkable.

ELECTROENCEPHALOGRAM

PROCEDURE PERFORMED:
Scalp electroencephalogram with photic stimulation and hyperventilation, sleep deprived.

HISTORY OF PRESENT ILLNESS:
A 49-year-old gentleman with history of seizure disorder with a left frontal cavernous hemangioma status post CyberKnife and status post surgical resection, currently on Lamictal and Vimpat. Please evaluate for seizures.

FINDINGS:
Background activity symmetrical in the parietooccipital region with a frequency of 12 Hz. There were intermittent focal sharp slowing captured intermittently from the F3 C3 region during this recording, also captured at times from the phase reversal at T3-T5 region. This occurred intermittently during this recording. Photic stimulation elicited occipital response at 2, 4, 6, 8, 10, 12, 14, 16, 18, 20, 24, and 30 Hz. Hyperventilation phase captured these sharp activities that are mentioned and also was captured some during the post hyperventilation phase.

IMPRESSION:
This is an abnormal electroencephalogram due to the presence of left frontocentral and left temporal sharp focal activity. This finding can be seen secondary to intracranial lesion presence or resection. Can also be suggestive of seizure focus from these areas. Clinical correlation is indicated. This study captured awake and drowsy state.

DD: 10/01/2012 12:22:28
DT: 10/01/2012 12:35:31
SGSNASHHSC; Job#1321559

Reason for Exam: Cavernoma
Exam Date: 3/4/10

MRI SCAN OF THE BRAIN WITH AND WITHOUT CONTRAST

CLINICAL INFORMATION: Cavernoma, followup.

FINDINGS: There is a prior study available dated 11/13/09.

Again noted is a focus of predominantly decreased T1 and T2 signal intensity in the superior frontal gyral region on the left, just anterior and superior to the cingulate sulcus. This finding is not significantly changed when compared with the prior exam and is consistent in appearance with a cavernous malformation.

Otherwise, there is no intra or extra-axial fluid collection, midline shift, mass effect, hemorrhage, hydrocephalus, or acute ischemia seen. No definitive signs of abnormal enhancement are seen following contrast administration.

Minimal nonspecific white matter disease is seen. This is not significantly changed from the prior study.

Vascular flow voids are grossly normal on T1 and T2 weighted images.

IMPRESSION:
1.   Findings are consistent with a cavernous malformation in the left superior frontal gyrus with no significant interval change from 11/13/09.
2.   Otherwise, no focal mass, hemorrhage, hydrocephalus, or acute ischemia is seen.

Dad-

I love the fact that you are writing a journal because it is much more personal than a biography.

For the first fifty or so pages, I wanted to cry the whole way but that's okay because for the rest of the journal, humor is very much brought into the situation.

You are appealing to ethos (emotions), logos (logical), and pathos (ethics). You tie all three components together beautifully.

Your journal is basically a part of your life's story so don't hold anything back and like you said, "this story is not supposed to be pretty" so let them cry because I did. And it's fine if you go on 200 more pages filling in more details.

I also love how everything isn't in order, it is but it isn't. I read your journal in one sitting and I already know your story, for the most part, but it is interesting so I read it all at once.

I think, once this journal is published, many people will understand epilepsy even though they don't show it.

And something written is easier to remember than my senior presentation on epilepsy.

I made various comments throughout and they are just suggestions of what I would do. Use them or throw them away.

I really hope this helps.

I love you!
All the Best,
Kelly

many need to hear the truth and good
news you convey.
Continued blessings!

Shalom,
Katharine

8 July 2014

Dear Fr. Choyce,
A friend forwarded your
article about disability to me. Thank
you for sharing this sermon with the
wider world. It is definitely not boring!
I hope you will continue to share your
gifts with the Church and the world —

Special Thanks:

The Rev. Dr. Hunter Huckabay

The Rev. Dr. Howard Kempsell, Jr.

The Rev. Duane Nettles and Annunciation Mission in New Orleans

The Rev. Raymond Souza

The Rt. Rev. Dean E. Wolfe

The Rev. Dr. William Breedlove and Good Shepherd Episcopal Church in Hayesville, NC

Brent Darnell for his encouragement of me to pursue publication.

Rick and Lisa Franklin

Susan Reid for her priceless help in editing this manual twice.

Frances Patton Statham for her invaluable editing help.

The Cavernous Malformation Support Network

For the incalculable family and friends who never gave up on me and continue to keep me in their prayers.

CPSIA information can be obtained
at www.ICGtesting.com
Printed in the USA
BVOW06s1507040118
504324BV00001B/47/P